A CRITICAL ANALYSIS

OF THE

PHILOSOPHY OF EMILE MEYERSON

BY

GEORGE BOAS

GREENWOOD PRESS, PUBLISHERS

NEW YORK 1968

First Greenwood reprinting, 1968

Library of Congress catalogue card number: 68-55099

Printed in the United States of America

FOREWORD

Some explanation is only fitting for the appearance of a critical analysis of the works of M. Meyerson by one who is neither a scientist nor particularly versed in logic. The following essay was conceived as an attempt to expound in an impartial manner the writings of this thinker, whose importance seemed underestimated in America. It was felt that such an exposition could have only the happy result of stimulating scholars to read him and of spreading his influence where it was greatly needed.

As the study continued, certain problems of a philosophical order began to arise and, though M. Meyerson himself was good enough to answer some of them in conversation with the writer, others remained unsolved. As a consequence this essay has taken on a critical character which was unforeseen at the time of its inception. Nevertheless the critical portions are still subordinated to the expository purpose of the whole, and only those are retained which seem to their author suggestive of possibly valuable theorems in the philosophy of science.

This foreword should not terminate without a word of thanks to M. Meyerson who during the winter of 1928-1929 gave me generously of his time and patience. This, however, does not mean that he has either seen or approved of any of the views expressed. I am also happy to record here my thanks to my friend, Richard Tolman, and to my colleagues and graduate students at the Johns Hopkins University, whose discussions have unfailingly helped to clarify my ideas.

G. B.

CONTENTS

PAGE

Foreword iii

Part One: Identité et Réalité.............. 1

Part Two: De l'Explication dans les Sciences 58

Part Three: La Déduction Relativiste...... 118

PART ONE

Identité et Réalité

The program of Emile Meyerson's investigations is to discover inductively the *a priori* principles of human thinking. By "*a priori*" M. Meyerson does not mean those principles which are necessary to thinking in the sense that the human mind will never be able to operate without them, but those principles without which the human mind has not operated to date and which are not discovered by it in experience itself.[1] Such an investigation requires obviously a number of concrete and intelligible examples. They are found in that record of human thinking which is known as natural science. Such an analysis ought to reveal the structure of thought in action and, by extension, not only the thought of trained scientists, but also that of common sense.

The outcome of his study is the conviction that two great principles control man's interpretation of na-

[1] M. Meyerson defines an *a priori* notion as "une notion instinctive de notre esprit que le raisonnement ultérieur ne ferait que dégager." (*Identité et Réalité,* 148). If the notion is really instinctive, the question of its necessity becomes one of the mutability of human nature. Have we any evidence of human thinking's ever changing in the past? We have at least the evidence afforded by M. Lévy-Bruhl's researches into primitive mentality. The reader must be cautioned not to be led astray by M. Meyerson's use of "*a priori*" as "purely deductive" or "formal" in Ch. III, IV, V, into thinking that his definition of "*a priori* notions" has changed.

ture. One of these he calls "the principle of legality," the other "the principle of causality."[2]

The principle of legality is, as its name suggests, the principle upon which natural law is based. A natural law is a statement of the form that any given event always occurs in such and such a way, e. g., water boils at 100° Centigrade; at a constant temperature the pressure and the volume of a gas vary inversely; the gravitational force between two bodies varies directly as the product of their masses and inversely as the square of the distance between them. The peculiarity of laws is that they hold good of any sample in the universe of discourse and always hold good.

Thus in the first place in order to formulate a law, one must be able to generalize.[3] In the second place

[2] *Identité et Réalité,* Paris, 1926 (2d ed.), ch. I. This work will be cited as *IR*. M. Myerson's other books, *De l'Explication dans les Sciences* (I use the edition in one volume, Paris 1927, original date 1921), and *La Déduction Relativiste,* Paris 1925, will be referred to as *ES* and *DR* respectively.

[3] M. Meyerson (*IR* 4) declines to discuss the epistemological question implied by generalization. This seems to the present writer a great pity. For it can be shown that on the whole people are inclined to believe that to generalize means to unite in a single class objects which have similar properties. These similar properties are then hypostatised and by means of a metaphor drawn from the comportment of the physical objects of common sense, they are endowed with a kind of persistency which raises more problems than it settles. The most important of these problems is whence these similar properties come and whither they go, as if (like physical objects) they had to come from somewhere and go somewhere. We see the unfortunate effect of such a habit of thought in such philosophical problems as that of the relation of mind and body, in which it is customary to take for granted not that the properties of minds must be con-

it involves the conviction that the future will reproduce the past, or better, that time is irrelevant to the occurrence of events. This, although M. Meyerson does not state it so, is equivalent to the statement that events are completely determined by a set of discoverable factors internal to them, none of which is time. The lawfulness of nature may not of course be complete, yet no scientist ever doubted its completeness. Given a set of conditions, the scientist expects a certain event to occur and if it did not occur, would insist either that all the conditions were not present or that some unsuspected condition was present which neutralized the action of the others.

It is true that prediction is necessary for action. We could perform no act successfully if the future did not reproduce the past nor would we consciously act if we did not expect the future to reproduce the past (*IR* 9). Action, moreover, is an animal necessity. Yet this, in spite of Comte, does not limit science to that which is useful, for the simple reason that we have no way of telling what may be useful and what may not be. The originators of the study of conic sections could in no way have foreseen their usefulness to the modern navigator nor could Leeu-

ditioned but that they must pre-exist somehow in their conditions. Since they have traits which are incompatible with those of their conditions, a problem arises which is obviously insoluble. In such a situation two courses are open: (1) to deny the incompatibility of the traits or (2) to deny the assumption of pre-existence. The course usually followed is the first with the results which every student of the history of thought knows.

wenhoek—to insert an example of our own—have foreseen the pasteurization of milk. But it does suggest a limitation of a practical nature to which M. Meyerson does not give full recognition.

M. Bergson seems to have demonstrated that the so-called immediate data of experience are the result of an analysis of perceptions and are, therefore, not either genetically prior to the percepts nor yet ostensibly (though they may be really) corresponding to any ontological reals independent of themselves. If this demonstration be well taken, then although there may be good reasons for accepting some kind of ontological reals in one to one correspondence (or even identical) with the percept—this would be a sort of naive realism—what ground would we have for accepting the existence of " scientific objects " ? These are constructed not to explain the percept, but to explain the sense data, and were the sense data different they too would be different. An examination of the history of theories of light and sound will amply demonstrate this. What harm, it will be replied, can this do, since our percepts are compounds of immediate data?

The answer is obvious. To put it in its briefest form, an analysis is teleological. Its results are functions of certain interests which the analyser happens to have at the moment of analysis, which interests—expressed in the form of working hypotheses—determine the sort of thing one is looking for and naturally the sort of thing one finds. Even in chemistry, which has become the *locus classicus* for examples of analysis, the tests selected determine in certain cases whether one discovers instances of a given element or its isotopes. Lead, e. g., reacts identically to one set of tests, variously to another set. That it retains the same name throughout is due to an historical accident. For had the discovery of radioactivity been pre-Lavoisierean—which was hardly possible—the isotopes of lead might very likely have been each given a separate name and the question would then have arisen in the XIXth Century how they could have similar reactions to the now standard chemical tests although different elements.

When one examines the analyses of human percepts, one sees how practical the tests are. They are naturally pervaded by the human equation and, although we know that our sensory equipment is not that of other animals, that there are sensory possibilities of which we are not aware, that some animals utilize senses with a degree of perspicuity unknown among human beings and rely but little upon senses which we consider of major importance, that even among humans beings there is a disconcerting range of individual difference, some perceiving distinctions where others perceive similarity, yet we persist (and justly persist) in believing that the world of scientific objects constructed to explain these sensations is the real world.[4] We know, however, that this world of scientific objects is devised primarily not to ex-

[4] Cf. *IR*, pp. 331-332.

plain all our senses but those upon which we usually rely, namely vision and touch. This can be seen by imagining what kind of world would be devised by an animal in which odors were predominant. If his sense of odor resembled ours, is it likely that his world would be one of shapes and weights? What suspicion of shapes and weights could ever arise in his mind? No, a fluidity of contour, impermanence and evanescence of being would be the rule, and fixity and rigidity the exception.

If this be so, does it prove that science is practical? At least it indicates that science is not irrelevant to our animal constitution and that it is oriented towards making the world harmonious with our nature. But what could be more practical than that? It is obviously not practical in the same sense that believing in immortality because it makes for human happiness is practical. But it is practical and not purely contemplative in the sense that an animal other than man might not recognize its claim to truth. It is a world constructed for the satisfaction of human interests, the only world that we can see and touch *at least in imagination,* in which the space is entirely a visual and tactual space, and in which the data of the other senses are first translated into visual and tactual terms before being absorbed into science.[5]

[5] Cf. the almost universal rule of devising visual instruments of precision, for the recording even of those phenomena normally perceived by some sense other than vision—temperature, for instance, or density.

The practical value, therefore, of the physical sciences is their assuring us that the world is essentially such as we see it and touch it, all due allowances made for individual differences and impermanences. We are more at home in such a world than in one whose essence would appear foreign to us and hostile to our modes of behaviour. That science has often had that purpose even consciously is witnessed by the care which scientists have had to assure their readers that their conclusions, though apparently strange, are really in accordance with common sense. They cannot be blamed for this, for were science at odds with common sense to the extent, say, of substituting the data of odor for those of vision and touch, no one would understand it and it would be the most futile of human enterprises. That is why it is so easy for neo-Hegelians to prove that theory and practice are not contradictory.

This type of practicality is, as I say, not considered by M. Meyerson, nor is it of any particular interest if one means by science physics. Hence we shall not continue the discussion at this point, but return to an exposition of *Identité et Réalité*.

The principle of legality, that time is irrelevant to law, is complemented by the principle of causality, that time is irrelevant to things. The scientist believes that just as objects can move freely about in space without essential change, so they can move about in time.[6] This principle is foreshadowed in the traditional phrase, *causa aequat effectum,* the principle of sufficient reason, which implies that something pre-existent to the effect can wholly explain why the effect is thus and so rather than otherwise. If the cause equals the effect, both growth and diminution must be explained away as appearance and the Lucretian formula, *ex nihilo nihil,* accepted with perfect literality.

These two principles, M. Meyerson argues, are not discovered but presupposed. Our laws, in the first place, do not apply to the objects of experience but to ideal objects. The very subject of law, the generalized concept, pure silver, the mathematical lever, the perfect gas, the ideal crystal, are constructions of thought, abstractions created by a theory (*IR* 20).[7]

[6] The reconciling of the principle of relativity with this is discussed in *La Déduction Relativiste,* which will be analysed in *Part Three.*

[7] This seems to the present writer to require a certain qualification, to which M. Meyerson could agree without changing this part of his theory. The abstractions which are made by modern science seem more and more to be based upon statistical groupings. When the "average" reading is accepted as the real measurement, it is not an abstraction of a quality equally present in all the objects studied but is a mathematical operation performed upon the measurements actually taken. Pure silver could be replaced by the most frequently found silver, though that would not account for the preliminary purification of it, or else by an imaginary term interpolated as the median in a series of real samples of silver, as the triangle the sum of whose angles equals 180° is interpolated as the median in a series of physical triangles, as a median from which they vary in the plus and minus directions. These are as "ideal," to be sure, as "abstractions," but in a different way. That difference is important in discussing the theory of persistent identity if not here.

That we can apply our laws directly to reality is due to the grossness of our senses and instruments. And in fact such an application succeeds at all only because we carefully remove all possible interference on the part of nature. " Quiconque a travaillé dans un laboratoire se rappelle avec combien de peine on parvient d'abord à réaliser les expériences en apparence les plus simples indiquées dans les manuels. Avec le temps l'habitude se crée, on prend les précautions d'une manière de moins en moins consciente et l'on arrive à croire que les expériences de vérification se font pour ainsi dire toutes seules, sans que nous ayons à contraindre la nature; de même que l'astronome, à force d'avoir observé et calculé les mouvements des astres, arrive à *voir* que la lune tombe sur la terre. N'empêche qu'en réalité, pour tout observateur non prévenu, ces deux corps restent à peu près à la même distance. A l'égard du phénomène directement observé, la loi n'est jamais que plus ou moins approchée; à l'aide de corrections successives, nous tâchons d'en adapter progressivement l'ensemble de plus en plus étroitement à la véritable marche de la nature. Mais il faut observer que ces nouveaux apports modifient sans cesse la science existante. La physique ne progresse pas comme la géométrie, qui ajoute de nouvelles propositions définitives et indiscutables aux propositions définitives et indiscutables qu'elle possédait déjà; elle progresse parce que, sans cesse, l'expérience fait éclater de nouveaux désaccords entre les lois et les faits. La loi est une construction idéale qui exprime, non pas ce qui se passe, mais ce qui se passerait si certaines conditions venaient à être réalisées.'' (*IR* 21 f) To be sure nature must be ordered to give us generalized concepts, but these concepts are not an exact image of nature. We simplify their temporal relations, maintaining that they are always true (*IR* 26). But that presupposes the homogeneity of time. We do not discover its homogeneity, but we assume it in order to utilize the principle of legality.

Space is likewise simplified (*IR* 27). We could erect laws which would be functions of space.[8] But we affirm that space is also indifferent to laws, asserting that they hold good elsewhere. We transfer these two properties to things in utilizing the principle of causality. Yet we know that objects cannot move about in time and we have no proof of their ability to move about freely in space. On the other hand, as Poincaré has noticed, the very existence of geometry probably depended originally on the ability of things to do just that and we assume it without further question. (We might suggest, as friendly critics of the human mind, that if free motion in space is an assumption, it can be criticised by its fruits, just as the assumption of absolute position was criticised. If it leads to greater intelligibility, then well and good; but if it is a source of problems greater than those it strive to solve, then there is

[8] This, in a measure, is what happens in the general theory of relativity.

reason to reject it, however universal its adoption has been to date).

What then is the fundamental difference between the principles of legality and causality? " La loi énonce simplement que, les conditions venant à se modifier d'une manière déterminée, les propriétés *actuelles* du corps doivent subir une modification également déterminée; alors que, de par le principe causal, il doit y avoir égalité entre les causes et les effets, c'est-à-dire que les propriétés primitives, plus le changement des conditions, doivent égaler les propriétés transformées " (*IR* 35). In other words legalism makes no assumptions about the past properties of the body but simply records the changes, i. e., the appearance and disappearance of present properties as the body changes. Causalism, on the other hand, assumes that in the past properties will be found an *explanation* of the present properties, just as in the present properties will be found an explanation of the future properties. But strictly speaking there ought to be equality between the two, which means that fundamentally the change ought to be apparent rather than real. In order to make the change apparent only, the scientist tries, as we shall see, to interpret all change as purely spatial. But according to his causal postulate spatial change is neutral as to an object's properties.

The principle of causality like that of legality is not corroborated by experience (*IR* 35). All the objects we know change continually as we do ourselves.

We need little pressure to admit that even things which seem least mutable are in reality undergoing slow but nevertheless important transformations. Its real source is in our thirst for knowledge. When we have determined the existence of some unchanging substance under the mutability of events, we feel that we have made the course of nature intelligible. It is made intelligible since reasoning is the substitution of identicals for one another. The principle of identity is *le vrai moule où l'homme coule sa pensée* (*IR* 37) and by means of the principle of causality, man grasps identities in the physical world. Even though these identities are creatures of his own fiat, he is satisfied by them, for in so far as they serve to identify cause and effect their fictitious character is of no importance.[9] The greatest case of this is found in things whose one difference will be spatial position.

[9] This is another instance of the "practicality" of science. Reasons can be given—and curiously enough are given by M. Meyerson himself—to illustrate the weakness of many of our conceptions, i. e., inertia, the ether, energy, etc. These conceptions I call "weak" because they involve either self-contradictory properties (the ether) or properties which cannot be rendered imaginable (inertia, the transfer of energy, *IR* 148). Yet because they exteriorise certain intellectual demands, we accept them. In other words we are, as was Zeno the Eleatic, faced with the problem of choosing between Reason and Observation. We, like Zeno, choose Reason. M. Meyerson's explanation of this is that it renders things *intelligible*. The present writer suggests that it renders things consistent by denying the variability discovered by observation. But if that variability were found to be lawful, statistical generalizations at least would be afforded without the assumptions needed to satisfy the principle of causality.

II

Although it has been maintained (*IR* 55) that all phenomena can be explained as functions of self-identical entities moving about in space, mechanism has never been universally applied to reality. It is really a postulate rather than an empirical generalization. We know how far biology is from explaining the phenomena under its scrutiny by spatial dislocations; we know how wide a gap there is between the atom of chemistry " avec ses multiples et mystérieuses qualités qui, tout aussi mystérieurement, en engendrent d'autres dans la molécule " (*IR* 57) and the atom of physics " dont la caractéristique essentielle est de ne posséder qu'une seule propriété, la masse, et de ne connaître qu'un seul mode d'action " (*Ib.*). In physics itself the mechanical theory is complete only in the explanation of gaseous bodies and in spite of the work of Hertz and his successors, no one can pretend that all forms of energy have been completely interpreted as modes of one form. This, to be sure, does not mean that mechanism will never be entirely successful, since the past of science is a record of continuous simplification.

Yet an obstacle remains which illuminates for us the heart of the whole problem. Mechanism, as we have said, always interprets change as motion (IR 62). But in motion two factors have been recognized, something which may be called " mass," and something which may be called " force." These two factors have formed the nuclei of two types of kinetic theory, (a) corpuscular theories which assert the existence of mass and motion, (b) dynamic theories which assert the existence of force and motion. A third type of theory which has asserted both mass and force has existed, it is true, but presents all the difficulties of each of the others plus the problem of their reconciliation in one. These difficulties M. Meyerson now proceeds to expound with a view to showing that each contains an irreducible puzzle.

Corpuscular theories, he points out, have been undoubtedly the most popular, since the very concept of "force" seems scandalous. They go back in the form of atomism to the twelfth century B. C. in the philosophy of Kanâda and somewhat later in the Jains (*IR* 87).[10] The corpuscles posited have the essential characteristic, as we have said, of mass and act by impact (*IR* 63). Yet in order to act by impact, they must not only be elastic and impenetrable, both of which properties need explanation for obvious reasons, (*IR* 63-68) but have shape as well (*IR* 68). They must be elastic in order to rebound when struck; but elasticity presupposes deformation and a heightening of temperature. The corpuscles—say, the molecules of a gas—cannot be deformed by definition and cannot have any temperature individually since heat is produced by their motion. Moreover, if they have shape, they must obviously

10 M. Meyerson bases his account of these theories on Mabilleau's *Histoire de la philosophie atomistique,* 1896.

be made up of smaller bits of matter—considerations of the " relativity " of size are irrelevant here—and hence can lose and acquire energy, in which case they are no longer perfectly elastic. At times, as in certain pages of Newton (*IR* 68), the hardness of the corpuscles is emphasized at the expense of the elasticity. But if they have any extension in space at all, their absolute hardness requires an explanation; for they must have some internal structure, not being punctiform, and hence it would be simply an accident that no force exists great enough to shatter them—physically not chemically. Thus both elastic corpuscles and impenetrable corpuscles raise problems as well as solving them.

An attempt was made by Boscovich to omit their extension and make them points, centres of force (*IR* 71). This was of course a switch to dynamism. This particular theory was unacceptable to the scientific mind for the simple reason that the radiating forces would be acting on nothing, since after all what is a point? We can form no image of it (*IR* 75) [11] and it involves action at a distance (*IR* 76). Action at a distance has proved inacceptable because

[11] M. Meyerson constantly raises the point that science has demanded *imaginable* theories. This cannot be doubted—nor can any of his conclusions—as an historical fact. But it leaves open the question of whether unimaginable theories—such as the quantum theories—are to die because no image can be formed of their subject matters. It also adds evidence to our remark in Section I, that science without being utilitarian in the vulgar sense of the word is, nevertheless, practical in assuring man that the world is at heart such as his most important sensations reveal it.

it is anti-spatial (*IR* 82); it makes bodies act where they are not. It supposes that a phenomenon conditions another and that nothing happens in between. To imagine an action we must suppose space and time continuous (*IR* 84). "Il est donc naturel de postuler que chaque endroit de l'espace n'est influencé que par le principe actif de l'endroit immédiatement voisin, tout comme chaque instant est conditionné par l'instant précédent et conditionne à son tour l'instant immédiatement postérieur. Et puis, si l'on abandonne cette restriction en ce qui concerne l'espace, si un corps peut réellement agir, produire une modification dans un endroit de l'espace sans rien modifier dans les espaces intermédiaires, pourquoi ne pourrait-il pas également *apparaître* dans un lieu éloigné, sans passer par les lieux qui séparent les deux positions? Pourquoi, puisqu'il agit simultanément partout, n'apparaîtrait-il pas simultanément dans deux endroits différents? Des suppositions de ce genre, si extravagantes qu'elles paraissent, ont d'ailleurs été formulées dès le XVIIIe siècle par Prémontval, et l'on peut voir dans le curieux petit ouvrage où elles sont contenues qu'elles se rattachent très directement au concept de l'action à distance. Il est tout aussi significatif à cet égard qu'un auteur récent, dans un livre qui présente d'ailleurs un réel intérêt, ait rattaché l'action de la gravitation à l'hypothèse de la quatrième dimension; c'est sur cette même supposition que les spirites fondent des idées dont la parenté avec celles de Prémontval ne saurait être niée, et l'on sait que Zoellner s'en est servi dans un dessein analogue. C'est qu'en effet l'action à distance est destructive de l'idée de l'espace. Cela se fait, comme l'a dit pittoresquement un philosophe célèbre, d'ailleurs partisan de l'action à distance, ' derrière le dos de l'espace.' La conception est anti-spatiale ou au moins *aspatiale.*" (*Ib.*)

But two comments are in order. (a) Even mechanical theories of the corpuscular type involve action at a distance, since the contiguity of two masses is never so complete that they fuse. Not only did Malebranche some years ago make this clear but M. Meyerson himself has emphasized it in analysing the problem of the interaction of two impenetrable bodies (*IR* 70). Why is action at a great distance any more difficult to conceive than action at a small distance? It is true, to be sure, that if the action is not really at a distance but produced by disturbances in a medium—the air, the ether, etc.—that these disturbances may die out after a certain distance as sound waves do. But that of course is not to the point.

(b) Is the resistance to action at a distance anything more than habit? M. Meyerson, relying on history, believes it is. He believes that its anti-spatiality justifies the physicists' antagonism to it (*IR* 85) and cites the general theory of relativity as proof that they will do their utmost to eliminate it (*IR* 80 f). But we may add the comment of Mr. Bridgman whose reputation as a scientist no one will care to deprecate.

"To many minds the concept of action at a distance is absolutely abhorrent, not to be tolerated for an instant. Such an intolerable situation is avoided by the invention of a medium filling all space, which transmits a force from one body to the other through the successive action on each other of its contiguous parts. Or the dilemma of action at a distance may be avoided in other ways, as by Boscovich in the eighteenth century, who, in order to explain gravitation, filled space with a triply infinite horde of infinitesimal projectiles. Now of course it is a matter for experiment to decide whether any physical reality can be ascribed to a medium which makes gravitation possible by the action of its adjacent parts, but I can see no justification whatever for the attitude which refuses on purely *a priori* grounds to accept action at a distance as a possible axiom or ultimate of explanation. It is difficult to conceive anything more scientifically bigoted than to postulate that all possible experience conforms to the same type as that with which we are already familiar, and therefore to demand that explanation use only elements familiar in everyday experience. Such an attitude bespeaks an unimaginativeness, a mental obtuseness and obstinacy, which might be expected to have exhausted their pragmatic justification at a lower plane of mental activity.

"Although it will probably be fairly easy to give intellectual assent to the strictures of the last paragraph, I believe many will discover in themselves a longing for mechanical explanation which has all the tenacity of original sin. The discovery of such a desire need not occasion any particular alarm, because it is easy to see how the demand for this sort of explanation has had its origin in the enormous preponderance of the mechanical in our physical experience. But nevertheless, just as the old monks struggled to subdue the flesh, so must the physicist struggle to subdue this sometimes nearly irresistible, but perfectly unjustifiable desire. One of the large purposes of this exposition will be attained if it carries the conviction that this longing is unjustifiable, and is worth making the effort to subdue." [12]

Since after all any action is bound to be action at some distance and since at least one representative scientist feels no hesitation in accepting it when discovered, there is reason to hope that some day science in general will attempt to point out when a distance becomes too small to be a distance or will relegate the question to the limbo of lost causes.

M. Meyerson in spite of the difficulty of defining " action at a distance " feels that the " aspatiality " of dynamism justifies the resistance of the physicists (*IR* 85). Though atomism—or " corpuscularism "—also involves difficulties, it is more congenial to the human mind, as is evidenced by its antiquity and its persistency.

It is congenial because it *explains*. The world seems to us as in a constant state of change. Yet the causal postulate asserts just the opposite; we feel a need for *understanding* things, and we can understand only by positing identity in time. Therefore we assert that the change is superficial and overlies an identity which alone is real. We *perceive* a difference where we must *conceive* identity. To make the situation rational, " Je puis supposer que les éléments des choses sont restés les mêmes, mais que leur arrangement s'est modifié " (*IR* 99). As this arrangement is conceived as spatial, and as we do not consider displacement to be a change (*Ib.*), we eat

[12] *The Logic of Modern Physics,* N. Y. 1927, pp. 46 f.

our cake and have it too. But since these entities which preserve their identity and give rise to the appearance of change are imperceptible, and since they must be solid matter, they must be " forcément des ultra-solides immodifiables, par conséquent impossibles à briser, à diviser mécaniquement, des atomes " (*IR* 100). This reduction of change to the displacement of permanent entities has to be sure, often been unconscious. The scientist reasons thus without knowing why, which may be another proof of its aprioricity. We argue that of all phenomena, only impact is explicable; it seems " quite clear and intelligible " (*IR* 105); therefore if we succeed in making it fundamental to all other phenomena, they in turn will take on an air of intelligibility. We postulate persistence and the least inexplicable persistence is that of the material particle (*IR* 106). It is not entirely comprehensible, but is the best offered to us.

The charm of atomism may be seen in its application to the biological sciences, if we may supplement the illustrations of M. Meyerson. Two of the best examples are the social atomism of Hobbes and the psychological atomism of the Associationists (or their French analogues, the Idéologues). Hobbes's social theory is obviously a translation of the physical theories of Galileo into social terms. The law of inertia is duplicated in the " state of nature " in which each individual follows his own path unless acted upon by another individual. That the paths intersect is to be expected from the geometry which it was Hobbes's boast that he knew so well. That intersection and the resulting collision were the state of warfare. The myth of the social compact sought to explain psychologically the harmony of paths in civilized society, but the resultant picture of the absolute monarch controlling paths of his subjects is duplicated later in Newton in the picture of the solar system, in which the orbits of the planets are compounded of their being pulled towards the sun and pursuing their own straight paths. That the political scientists' problem was to describe conditions as they existed in actual society seems self-evident to us of to-day; yet in the 17th and 18th centuries it seemed as necessary to explain those conditions as products of logically—if not temporally—prior conditions as it does to the physicist to explain the motions of the solar system by the motions of the individual bodies composing it. This is witnessed by the almost universal custom of analysing society into the men and women who seemingly composed it. When societies—such as those of the American Indians—could be found which appeared to exemplify a "state of nature," so much the better; but when they could not be found, the political scientist was no more seriously worried by this than the physicist is by his failure to find bodies moving in free space.

The theory of associationism is a clearer example. Although we are daily made conscious of the fact that the so-called elements of perception are not found " in " the perception[13] and that the repetition of an experience is strictly speaking impossible, yet the analytic psychologist is not thereby hindered from pursuing his research and elaborating his analyses. We accept *a priori* the postulate that persistent simple things can by what can only metaphorically be called a rearrangement explain the occurrence of highly complex things and the ineptitude of the postulate disturbs us much less than the lack of an explanation. Nothing that ever existed could be immediately perceived to be complex. It is perceived as it is and its complexity is an inference subsequent to manipulation.[14] But that inference is based in turn upon the atomic postulate, that certain entities persist and by external relations to one another produce other entities, although " analysis " reveals only two successive but not genetically related events. The externality of the relations is presumably proved by the reversibility of the productions in physics and chemistry. But even when—as in political science and psychology—the productions are essentially irreversible, the postulate is retained.

This procedure seems to be necessitated by linguistic usage and by the logic of Aristotle (which is, it is platitudinous to remark, based upon linguistic usage) and is paralleled in the metaphysics of observation.

[13] For that matter neither are the elements of chemistry. We find them by breaking up the compound and we infer that they must have been in it to come out of it.

[14] This approaches, I take it, what M. Bridgeman means by " operational."

By means of language we grow accustomed to the idea that a word retains its meaning regardless of its context. Mr. Schiller has nevertheless acquainted us with the weakness of this idea by demonstrating how little it is corroborated in experience. Nevertheless it is a postulate necessary for formal reasoning and the present writer admits that he cannot see how to abandon formal reasoning entirely. But though we retain it, we need not conclude that the moving of verbal symbols in and out of propositions is a literal reduplication of the generative processes of nature. In fact we have good evidence that at least in biology growth does not proceed by the accretion of pre-existent elements at all but by their absorption and transformation into new things. None of this process—I am merely repeating commonplaces—could be revealed by a lateral cross-section of a living being. But all change, as M. Meyerson shows, is essentially irrational so that a science which deals primarily with processes will either be distorted beyond recognition by atomism or will renounce "explanation" altogether. It is the personal belief of the writer that the biological sciences have only made progress by this renouncement and that during the seventeenth and eighteenth centuries, when attempts were made to atomize or mechanize them—even by vitalists [15]—they dealt in myth rather than in fact.

[15] The vitalists have often had recourse to the trick of imagining an unchanging reality which would fulfill the same function as "matter" fulfills in physics. One finds this same trick performed in Hegel's theory of history or Freud's psychology. What are the life-force, the subconscious, the Idea, but that-which-endures-change-with-

The atomistic hypothesis seems to be justified by Aristotelian logic in the use that logic makes of the concept of essence. The Greeks, with the possible exception of the Sophists, were enamoured of the eternal and had of course good reason for believing the essences to be eternal. But they had no reason whatsoever for embodying the essences in matter and as everyone knows their explanations of how this occurred exhibited all the difficulties that the epistemology of Mr. Santayana exhibits. It is obvious that the essence of " motion " as a thought or a symbol cannot move but that does not imply that motion is not motion. Yet so accustomed are we to seeking the essences in matter, that we invent them if we do not find them. And as the essences are atomistically related to one another—except possibly in the Neo-Platonistic hierarchy of being—we assume that the things they symbolize are atomistic also.

The metaphysics of optics and acoustics aids all this by its assumption that the fleeting glimpses which we have of nature in sensation are somehow or other—how has never been very clearly defined—

out-changing, that which is identical throughout time and which *explains,* which acts as a subject of change? How can one understand the action of a living body, says the vitalist (of a certain type) unless there is an agent directing and controlling it; how explain memory and anticipation without something which remembers and anticipates; how explain the development of thought without a thought to develop? It should be added to the credit of M. Bergson that he was almost unique among vitalists in insisting on the reasons why we posit a life-force and on the insufficiency of the concept—at least for philosophy.

either atomic bits of consciousness or in one to one correspondence with material states which are atomic. By the correlation of various people's sensory experiences with a single scientific object a great simplification has been brought about in "natural philosophy" and one would be very foolish to deprecate it. At the same time it is well to be aware of its basic reason. That, I take it, is the equating of non-contradiction with "reality." Otherwise there would have been no hindrance to the acceptance of the data of sense as the "real objects." This hindrance may possibly be eliminated by the usual methods of positivism or by the postulates of "objective relativism." It is certain nevertheless that mankind has never been positivistic nor relativistic in its actual treatment of perception.

Whether these three influences towards atomism will ever cease is a subject for speculation alone. M. Meyerson ought to be congratulated no doubt rather than censured for not indulging in it. The writer will himself in another study yield to the temptation of such a speculation even though its results be in the least solid realm of possibility.

III

Since the principle of mechanism demands the *persistence* of something in order to equalize causes and effects, M. Meyerson next tries to show how that demand has been satisfied in the history of science. In the three chapters subsequent to his analysis of mechanism, he treats the three most famous principles of conservation, that of inertia, of matter, of energy.

After defining the three terms he attempts to show whether the principles are *a priori* or *a posteriori.* If they were *a priori,* they would be found in all discussions germane to the subject. Yet their history shows that though they were at times suggested in ancient physics, their precise formulation did not occur until modern times: the principle of inertia in the seventeenth century, the conservation of matter in the eighteenth, the conservation of energy in the nineteenth. Therefore they cannot be said to be instinctive.

At the same time he shows that they are not proved empirically. The principle of inertia involves the concept of " velocity " which can only be expressed as a quotient; but a quotient is nothing which can be preserved throughout time and in this case happens to be the quotient derived by dividing time by distance. By the mathematical device of " limits," one can derive the concept of " velocity at a point." This appears to generate something which can persist, be multiplied and divided. Yet what has occurred is the metamorphosis of a *relation* into a *state* which endures as a kind of substance and can be preserved. Such a *state* is certainly never found in experience, which obviously reveals nothing but the spatio-temporal relation. Yet because its hypostatization permits us to stipulate an identity in time, because it satisfies our *causal tendency,* we feel more certain about it than about many of our empirical generalizations, so certain that some philosophers—Spencer, for instance (*IR* 130)—insisted that it was an *a priori* truth whose contradiction was inconceivable. Had they had the advantage of reading *Identité et Réalité* they would have found other philosophers not only who did not dream of it but who formulated its very opposite—Hipparchus and Benedetti and presumably the youthful Galileo (*IR* 132). Such principles, neither *a priori* nor *a posteriori,* which stipulate identity in time, even at the expense of transforming relations into terms, M. Meyerson will call " plausible."

The same examination is made of the conservation of matter and of energy. Matter has been identified with mass which in turn has been identified with weight and with " that which causes the displacement of another bit of matter " (*IR* 196). But weight which in Aristotle was one of the accidents of matter, like color or temperature, and could be gained or lost with no gain or loss in the " amount of matter," has been defined by us as the product of gravitation and mass. And mass as the property of displacing other bits of matter is so obscure a concept—usually indefinable in manuals of physics—that it is perhaps best called the constant coefficients which appear in mathematical expressions of the communication of velocities or accelerations between bodies. Yet that of course tells us nothing of its " nature " [16] and the fact that in the

[16] The " nature " of things is a concept which we cannot but feel that M. Meyerson should have analysed further, especially in view

Lorentz equations mechanical mass is not a constant shows us that it is possible to conceive it as accidental and not essential to matter (*IR* 202 f). Its conservation—when invoked—is again a plausible principle because we want to conserve matter and we shall conserve in physics whatever seems to us to be the essence of matter. But here again our experience introduces us to relations which we hypostatize into substances in order to appease our hunger for permanence.

The case of the conservation of energy is even more dramatic. Energy used to be defined as the capacity to produce an effect or do work (*IR* 204).[17] The principle of the conservation of energy demands that the total of energy in an isolated system remain the same. But we have two cases which seem to violate this principle: one—the acceleration of falling bodies—

---

of positivistic and pragmatistic attacks upon its significance. Have things any "nature" other than that revealed in their observed or inferred relations to other things? Do we really know any more about the "nature" of mass if we say it is "the amount of matter" or "the property of displacing other bits of matter" than if we accept it as an indefinable? In any event, whatever meaning the term will have will imply some criteria of the presence of mass or remain unknown to us, so that if no criteria are provided, the term is as good as undefined. Many people would deny that its being the *coefficients immuables, si les corps se communiquent des vitesses ou des accélérations* (*IR* 199f) was not its "nature." M. Meyerson himself agrees that the course of wisdom is perhaps to leave undetermined *la nature de l'action que les masses exercent les unes sur les autres* (*IR* 199), but has this action any "nature" other than that of being the said constant coefficients? Why should any other nature in the long run be sought for it? The question of the difference between "natures" and "behaviour" is continued in Part II below.

[17] But cf. *IR* 317.

in which energy seems to be created; one—the locking of a coiled spring—in which it seems to be destroyed. Hence the concept of " potential " energy is elaborated to reconcile these cases with the principle. (It will be noted that the principle is not transformed to be reconciled with observation.)

That this law is not only not empirically proved but that its empirical verification by Joule was not of an order that would have inspired confidence in most laws (IR 212) is clearly shown by M. Meyerson.[18] But there is a certain difficulty in capturing energy for experimental purposes which makes empirical demonstration difficult (*IR* 214). That is why we have to specify that the system in which the sum of the energy is constant be isolated. But furthermore, to prove it adequately would require a knowledge of all forms of energy (and, we may add, on our own account, a justification of their identification as " energy ") and such a knowledge has certainly never been in our possession in the past and shows no likelihood of being possessed by us in the future. Yet of its certitude we feel no doubt.

Like the other principles of conservation it is plausible. We demand that something be preserved in energetic changes, however vague our idea of what that something is.

" D'abord, au point de vue historique, . . . la conservation est postulée avant même que le concept ne

[18] A much more stable series of measurements was made by Rowland in his *Mechanical Equivalent of Heat.*

se précise. On *veut* que quelque chose se conserve, Descartes et ses contemporains l'affirment, tout en se trompant complètement sur la nature de ce qui se conserve. Il se peut que l'erreur soit d'origine expérimentale, mais il est certain que l'expérience de Mersenne qui fournissait le point de départ, à supposer même qu'elle fût exacte, n'autorisait pas, à beaucoup près, une généralisation aussi vaste. Il est tout aussi remarquable que, pendant toutes les discussions qui ont eu lieu au XVIIe et au XVIIIe siècle sur la question de la mesure de la force, mesure et conservation aient été absolument confondues. Si une force (nous disons une énergie) est susceptible d'exercer un certain effet, la force qui pourra exercer un effet identique devra être estimée égale à la première; mais il ne s'ensuit point que la force doive égaler son effet. Or, c'est au contraire cette seconde formule, comme il est aisé de s'en convaincre, qui est au fond des discussions dont nous venons de parler. Enfin, il est clair que la découverte de Mayer et de Joule ne faisait que substituer un concept de constance à d'autres, déjà préexistants, qu'elle détruisait par là même. Leibniz supposait indestructible l'énergie mécanique et, d'autre part, Deluc, Black et Wilke admettaient l'indestructibilité de la chaleur-matière. Ce que nous appelons le principe de la conservation de l'énergie a consisté à démontrer au contraire qu'aussi bien la chaleur que l'énergie mécanique, prises isolément, peuvent naître et périr, mais qu'alors la disparition de l'énergie mécanique est accompagnée de l'apparition d'une certaine quantité d'énergie calorique et vice versa.

" On arrive à des conclusions analogues en examinant de près le concept de l'énergie tel que nous le trouvons dans la science actuelle. Le concept de la masse n'est que l'expression du rapport suivant lequel les corps agissent les uns sur les autres. Cette action, en réalité, est strictement déterminée, c'est l'action mécanique: le rapport serait tout différent si nous prenions pour base l'action électrique ou calorique. Toutefois, par suite de la précellence que nous attribuons aux phénomènes du déplacement à l'égard de tous les autres sans exception, il est certain que le concept de masse nous apparaît comme revêtu d'une importance particulière. D'ailleurs, en vertu du principe d'inertie qui exprime que l'état du mouvement du corps est indifférent, pourvu que ce mouvement soit rectiligne et uniforme, nous avons la possibilité, pour déterminer le rapport en question, de partir d'un état initial qui nous apparaît comme identique: le repos relatif. Enfin, une expérience incessante nous fait connaître les rapports entre tous les corps qui nous entourent et un corps unique, toujours le même, la terre. C'est ce qui fait que la masse nous apparaît non plus comme un rapport entre deux corps, mais comme un coefficient s'attachant à chaque corps en particulier, comme une propriété du corps, après quoi la causalité se charge de la transformer en substance. Mais il n'en va pas de même de l'énergie; elle reste un rapport, et si l'on veut la concevoir comme une propriété, ce sera la propriété d'un système et non pas celle d'un corps . . . Même en restant dans le domaine purement mécanique, nous ne parvenons point à rattacher l'énergie, comme propriété, aux corps. Il suffit, pour s'en convaincre, de considérer la formule mathématique de l'énergie cinétique. Elle contient le carré de la vitesse; or, nous ne connaissons que des vitesses relatives. Toutes les masses terrestres qui nous entourent, vues du soleil, se déplacent avec une rapidité considérable, entraînées par le mouvement de la terre; de ce chef, elles possèdent donc une énergie cinétique énorme. Mais nous n'en tenons aucun compte, nous la traitons comme inexistante, à juste titre d'ailleurs, puisque, à moins d'une rencontre avec un bolide, elle ne peut en aucune façon intervenir dans ce qui se passe sur la terre. A plus forte raison le concept de l'énergie potentielle est-il inséparable de la considération d'un système: cette masse que je tiens dans ma main peut tomber sur le sol de ma chambre, dans la rue ou dans un puits, que je peux m'imaginer aussi profound que je veux; je puis aussi me figurer qu'elle tombera sur le soleil qui, incontestablement, l'attire, et la somme d'énergie que dégagera chacun de ces phénomènes sera très différente. Il est impossible de jauger d'avance, en ne considérant qu'un corps et non pas un système, quelle est la somme d'énergie qu'il est susceptible de dégager; celle-ci est proprement infinie, même à l'intérieur de chaque corps, car nous n'avons qu'à supposer les corps composés de centres de forces pour qu'en faisant coincider deux de ces centres, nous obtenions un travail infini. Lord Kelvin a introduit le terme d'*énergie intérieure totale* (*total intrinsic energy*) et bien des physiciens s'en sont servis à sa suite. Mais il faut se rappeler que cette grandeur est définie par rapport à un état considéré comme normal (*standard state*), elle est donc susceptible de prendre une valeur négative. Hertz fait remarquer à juste titre que cette supposition serait absurde pour une véritable substance, celle-ci bien entendu, ne pouvant être conçue que comme une grandeur positive, et que, dans ces conditions, l'énergie potentielle résiste à toute définition lui attribuant les propriétés d'une substance. Pour notre imagination la matière est quelque chose de réel et l'énergie n'est qu'une intégrale " (*IR* 230 ff). This long quotation may perhaps be an intrusion in an expository essay, but it sums up more clearly than I can hope to do in my own words M. Meyerson's conclusion.

There are two assumptions which make possible the principle of the conservation of energy and are not always as clearly articulated as might be. The first is that electricity, light, heat, and so on are all " forms " of the same thing called " energy." The question might very pertinently be asked of the physicist just how seriously he wishes this formula to be taken, not to mention its precise meaning. Mathematically it is easy to see that these various terms serve the same function as integrals but the statement of their all being " forms " of the same thing is not simply a metaphor. The present writer is incompetent to do more than raise this question, pointing out that when two things are said to be forms of a third thing, that third thing is usually a " substance " out of which the other two are made, through a structural differentiation, as O_2 and O_3 might be said both to be " forms " of oxygen. Are we to suppose that there is something called " energy "—otherwise unspecified—of which electricity, heat, light, etc., are forms, differing only in structure? It seems doubtful that such can be the real meaning of the physicist since the only energy he can observe is the forms. Yet the forms are not conserved; it is " energy " which is conserved.

The second assumption concerns the nature of potential energy. Its existence is needed in order that the dictum, *ex nihilo nihil,* be observed, for otherwise in the case of falling bodies and locked springs the energy could come from nowhere and go nowhere. Yet the only evidence of the presence of potential energy is its appearance in kinetic form after it has ceased to be potential. That the concept simplifies our thinking—if we do not worry about it—is no doubt true and, as M. Meyerson has demonstrated, it satisfies our causal tendency. But not only does it transform a relation into a " thing," it transforms it into a thing whose existence is dependent upon certain assumptions of methodology rather than inferred from the results of observation. It is not of course unique in either of these characteristics.

It may now be fitting to ask two questions which would seem inevitable to one reading *Identité et Réalité* in the light of the positivistic critique.

First, when M. Meyerson remarks that certain principles are not proved *a posteriori,* what does he mean by " prove "? It is certain that no irrefragable proof of anything has ever been offered to man, for the simple reason that somewhere there will be premises which are taken for granted. In the case of experimental science, how much proof can be demanded? One cannot erect an experiment without certain preliminary hypotheses, and it is indubitable that these hypotheses are only tentatively verified by the experiment even when it is successful. For formally experimentation is like an hypothetical syllogism in which one tries to conclude to the antecedent by asserting the consequent—which is of course fallacious. Therefore an experiment can disprove a proposition but can never prove one, unless one has prior knowledge that there are only two possible antecedents. Nevertheless we are dependent upon experiment for most of our scientific knowledge and though a good amount of it is used to disprove other people's theories, we never feel satisfied with our own until they are experimentally corroborated—witness the attempts to " prove " experimentally the general theory of relativity. This corroboration obviously cannot hope to do more than establish our theories tentatively, until a theory for other reasons better than ours is also corroborated by our experiments. Hence it is not surprising that the three principles of conservation are not conclusively proved *a posteriori*. What is? The question really is whether they have greater probability than their contradictories.

The second question concerns the meaning of "plausible." If plausible propositions depend for their plausibility upon their satisfaction of certain of our subjective needs, it is difficult to distinguish between this theory of science and that of certain pragmatisms. For in neither case is the truth of the propositions supposed to be based on correct inference from given premises—either self-evident or arbitrarily assumed as one chooses—or on correspondence with fact. It is on the contrary determined by human needs, so that science could be interpreted as a humanization of the world not merely in the sense discussed in section I above but in the sense that an intelligence other than human, even if capable of understanding our concepts, would see no particular reason for interpreting the universe as we do. In principle this is very similar to the standpoint of positivism—at least of Comte's particular brand—for after all whether the test of truth be social welfare [19] or intellectual comfort is a small matter. In

[19] Of course truth was determined by more than social welfare in Comte, but the drive towards positivism was an elimination of

other words this makes science an interpretation of the world and neither a description nor an explanation of it in the ordinary sense of those words. This is to be sure a very popular view of science at the present time and one which the present writer finds in part very sympathetic. It raises the very difficult problem of how observation and experimentation *verify* our beliefs and it also seems more harmonious with the philosophy which M. Meyerson is attacking than with that which he aspires to defend.

IV

We have now seen how science seeks to appease our appetite for enduring substances by postulating principles of conservation. But though substance is conserved, attributes change, and it still remains for science to show that a change in attributes is superficial and unimportant. It does that by asserting a perfect equivalence between cause and effect, so that one may be substituted for the other. Thus the causal series is not only *A* followed by *B*, but *A* equalling *B*. But if the cause and the effect are equivalent, the process of causation ought to be reversible and one ought to be able to pass as freely from *B* to *A* as from *A* to *B*. This was in fact the theory of Leibnitz as expressed in the formula, " L'effet intégral peut reproduire la cause entière ou son semblable " (*IR* 238).

knowledge which was not useful for " action " and by action Comte meant the special kind of action which would ameliorate according to his standards the quality of society.

That our experience itself affords no example of reversibility is clear. Our consciousness shows us an unchangeable flow of time, nor can we move against its current. Moreover, says M. Meyerson with justice (*IR* 239), to move back into the past would be to introduce a new element into the past which would make the present different from what it actually is. To modify the past seems contradictory to us. Moreover if such an attempt could be made, we should have to collect all the loss of energy which has occurred through friction—and there would always be some in any real case of change—and since that would be impossible we must conclude that any real, i. e., physical, reversible process is never found.

It is of course true that the physicist can by a process of extrapolation reach a point in which infinitely small results are produced by infinitely small amounts of energy, and apparently by the successive subtraction and addition of these infinitely small amounts of energy a reversible process will result, since no escape of energy can occur. Thus a spring stretched downward by a weight can on paper be made to move upward with no expenditure of a finite amount of energy by the successive substraction of infinitesimal amounts of the weight and made to stretch downward again by their successive addition. Yet such an example is obviously inapplicable to the real world, for by no stretch of the imagination can we conceive of the spring moving upward in space because of a series of substractions of infinitesimal amounts, for if it moved upward an infinitesimal distance each time, it would not move at all and no process of arithmetic has yet succeeded in producing a finite sum out of the addition of several infinitesimals. Moreover the infinitely small, though standing as a limit for our successive divisions of the weight on the string, is a limit which clearly cannot be reached. And finally we have no assurance that, though the subtraction of half the weight might send the spring upwards one half the distance, the subtraction of a very small amount—to say nothing of an infinitesimal—would send it up a proportional very small distance, for recent observations in physics have shown us that the "microscopic" realm does not always act according to the same laws as the macroscopic and that the simple arithmetical divisions might produce quite different effects.

Hence we must admit that there will always be a loss of energy in any real case when any finite amount of work is done and that consequently no physical process is really reversible. Yet rational mechanics reposes on the possibility of reversible action. The two sides of an equation must be equal; one must be able to substitute for the other. This is equivalent to the denial that these equations represent processes occurring in time. One can either say that time is thus made a dimension of space, following possibly Lagrange (*IR* 241), a dimension along which one can move in either direction—since it no longer has a direction—or one can repeat the thought which opened M. Meyerson's study, that in rational mechanics time is *irrelevant* to phenomena. This is a manifestation again of the causal principle, which demands an equality between antecedent and consequent (*Ib.*), a demand which cannot be satisfied if the equals-sign be not accepted literally. Thus rational mechanics satisfies our reason perfectly; its equations are like those of mathematics which represent no process but, so to speak, an equilibrium. At the same time it must be admitted to be the science *la plus éloignée de la réalité* (*IR* 237).

This is a situation which deserves notice. " Reality " in this context can only mean " appearance," or the experience of common-sense, and not that underlying world of substance or invariants which the Democritean tradition has been accustomed to call by that name. It is therefore an admission that the most satisfactory science is not necessarily the most faithful picture of reality, though elsewhere [20] the criterion of satisfactoriness has been our ability to picture, to imagine the facts described by science. We shall see, moreover, that M. Meyerson emphasizes the re-entrance of time into science through the second law of thermodynamics. Is it therefore not possible for the scientist to demand that his reasonings be more faithful to experience? What binds him to accept unquestioningly these formulæ whose inadequacy is so vividly pointed out to him? Is it

[20] Cf., e. g., *ES* 86 and *IR* 75.

impossible for him to devise an account of reality which will present a recognizable picture of it?

The answer is probably in the affirmative if he insist that the denotation of his symbols is a series of self-identical, unvarying substances like his symbols themselves. The Aristotelian logic made such a one to one correspondence between its concepts and their denotation and established the tradition, clearly foreshadowed even in Aristotle's earliest predecessors, that the world of reason was the world of reality and the world of sensation unreal. It could never have occurred to such people that contradiction between science and experience was to the detriment of science. This comes out clearly in the Eleatics. If motion be proved irrational, it must be held to be unreal; the fact that we experience motion would certainly never have seemed to Zeno disproof of his reasoning. Yet it comes natural enough to M. Meyerson, much as he doubts the possibility of reforming scientific thought, to speak of experience as reality and to point out how removed from it is rational mechanics. Certainly most modern thinkers would feel that this was to the discredit of rational mechanics. Yet there can be no doubt that they have all "corrected" experience in the same manner whenever they have geometrized it. Is there any way of correcting experience and retaining it as a criterion of validity?

If one retains experience, one must retain multiplicity, diversity, and process. No technique has yet been devised for purging the world of them. But it is certainly clear that just as in discursive thought a word must retain its meaning, so in science the properties of the things discussed must be immutable, the things must be externally related to one another or "atomic," and processes turned into equations. There is obviously no way of "reconciling" this situation or of controlling reason by experience. And yet the excesses of peripateticism in the middle ages and early Renaissance still linger in our memories as the penalty of not controlling reason by experience. But if experience is to be absorbed into science, it can only be by admitting the inadequacy of "reason." It seems to the present writer that such an admission is made whenever a scientist turns from the usual formal mathematics to statistics and the calculus of probabilities. The use of statistics is an abandonment of explanation, in M. Meyerson's sense of the word, for it retains the multiplicity of phenomena, holding that the law is true of the group and determined in part by the size of the group, the diversity of the phenomena, and by graphs it even retains the passage of time. There is therefore a technique of having science and having experience as well but at the sacrifice of the causal instinct. One can in Meyersonian terms have legality but not causality. Is there any reason to think that science is headed in that direction?

One cannot but feel that there is. For statistics, which originally was used in the biological sciences alone, has now found a home for itself in physics as well. As soon as a scientist argues that a molecule can go in any one of six directions, he has abandoned the attempt to " explain " in which direction it will go. It is no longer a question of why it took this direction rather than that but of calculating the number of directions it " can " take. But that presupposes that that number is more than one. We may say that " if we knew more about it " we should not need to use statistics. But (a) we do not and probably never shall know more about it, and (b) it is a gratuitous assumption that greater knowledge would reveal an " explanation " of the movement of these particles. When a case of eliminating statistics from molecular dynamics is advanced, then we may argue that it is a purely temporary phase in the history of science. But on the contrary there is every evidence that its use is increasing.

To return to our subject, the elimination of time in physics is paralleled by its elimination in chemistry. Each chemical formula states an operation to be sure but these operations are disguised as equations (*IR* 250). The = sign is theory and not practice. Practice gives us HgO heated, with mercury and oxygen as products. (In fact the very symbol, HgO, is theory and not observation.) The equation expresses this dynamic process as *une relation d'équivalence entre deux états statiques* (*Ib.*). Why are we not shocked by this disfiguration of experience? Because it allows us to see beneath the apparent diversity an identity (*IR* 251). " Water " is a wet, colorless liquid, relatively heavy, which prevents combustion; H_2O is a compound of two gases, one the lightest element known, inflammable, the other only 16 times heavier, aiding combustion. We can see how hydrogen and oxygen should have *come out of* H_2O, but not out of water. And we insist that if the electrolysis of water gives one hydrogen and oxygen, they must have been *in* the water previously to the electrolysis.

A chemical equation thus eliminates any real change. The elements on one side exist on the other side; the weight is the same, the energy is the same. All that has happened is a rearrangement in space of these elements. Whereas formerly they were hooked together in one way, now they are hooked together in another. But displacement is privileged (*IR* 253) and does not count as real change. Yet if we wished to be complete, we should eliminate even displacement. For motion is as *inconceivable* as any other kind of change and is indeed only made rational by means of the infinitesimal calculus which builds it up out of " tiny states of rest." " En somme, la science, dans son effort à devenir ' rationnelle,' tend de plus en plus à supprimer la variation dans le temps. Et l'on aperçoit clairement que l'empirisme ne saurait y être pour rien. En effet, l'instinct de la conservation exige la prévision; c'est donc l'évolution dans le temps qui nous intéresse surtout et il semble que la forme essentielle de la loi, de la règle empirique, devrait être celle d'une modification en fonction du temps. Or, il n'en est nullement ainsi. Si l'on trouve quantité d'énoncés en fonction du temps dans les sciences de l'être organisé, c'est qu'elles sont encore au début de leur évolution. Mais ces énoncés sont d'autant plus rares que la science est plus rationelle." (*IR* 256.)

If the task of explanation were pushed to its logical completion, all motion and all change would disappear, and the One of Parmenides would alone remain. Its immutability would be explained by the principle of temporal identity, but its unity would be still unaccounted for. M. Myerson then proceeds (*IR* ch. VII) to demonstrate how science has denied multiplicity as well as change. That it has denied it is shown from the time of the Eleatics on, when in spite of atoms, qualitative as well as quantitative, in spite of elemental diversity, matter is held to be basically one. This appears not only in Prout's hypothesis that hydrogen is the basic element, of which all the others are combinations, but also in such theories as those of Planck and Rutherford.[21] In fact chemists have never accepted the existence of many elements, as is illustrated with peculiar force in their desire for a mechanical interpretation of valence (*IR* 268). Their feeling has been shared by the philosophers of whom M. Meyerson cites impressive examples (*Ib.*).

[21] Cf. *La Déduction Relativiste,* § 202.

What now is the cause of this drive towards material unity? Not the principle that cause and effect are equal, for that would not imply that matter is homogeneous; it would necessitate simply that the cause be found " in " the effect, as is theoretically supposed to be the case in chemistry. In fact a diversity of elements would be of greater service to this theory (*IR* 269) since it would provide for more combinations.

Yet if we turn to the actual fact of becoming, more light is thrown on the necessity for material unity. In other words by a hidden use of Occam's razor, matter is left with the one property it needs in order to displace other bits of matter (*IR* 274). But that very property, does it not diversify matter? No, for it is an unimaginable property, and indeed when philosophers, such as Descartes and Locke, have enumerated the properties of matter, i. e., the primary qualities, we find them to be simply the properties of space. Locke, to be sure, includes " solidity " but " solidity " is in turn a *qualité occulte* and consequently one which has no place in a purely rational physics. The Cartesian theory is therefore more congenial to the scientific spirit than the Lockean and indeed finds itself completed (*IR* 279, n. 3) in the modern theories of relativity. This tendency " reduces " matter to space which is presumably homogeneous and thus accomplishes the unification of matter.[22]

[22] But what does the homogeneity of space consist in when it " contains " gravitational fields or when by the metaphor of space-

Proceeding thus we are faced with a world in which reality is annihilated (*IR* 285). " Car le temps et l'espace se sont dissous. Le temps, dont le cours n'implique plus de changement, est indiscernable, inexistant; et l'espace, vide de corps, n'étant plus marqué par rien, disparaît aussi (*Ib.*)." This is inevitable, since we have searched for the why of things in the principle of identity (*Ib.*). But how can identity explain both change and diversity? It obviously cannot. Hence science seems to exist as a means of reassuring us against experience, not as its explanation. It tells us that we need not fear the passage of time nor the diversity of fortune. All is one and one at all times. The rest is illusion. It preserves all the well tested virtues of Greek aristocratic thought and the modern English chemist who discovers a new set of isotopes joins hands with Parmenides of Elea in an unbroken tradition of absolute monism.

It would seem, we might venture to suggest, that science answers a question which was formerly supposed to be the peculiar problem of philosophy, namely, in what sense of the word is the world one? It obviously cannot explain how the one becomes

time, as in the general theory of relativity, velocities and hence masses vary as a function of *position?* Does the " reduction " of matter to space mean more than that we can deduce the behaviour of matter from its spatio-temporal properties, which may be a reduction of physics to geometry—by putting into geometry postulates which formerly belonged to physics or by defining physical terms by geometrical indefinables—but is certainly not a reduction of matter to space. But see Part III of this study.

many, for becoming is eliminated from reality. Hence the Renaissance insistance on checking deduction by experimentation is otiose and indeed, as we have suggested in Section III above, experimentation can disprove generalizations but never prove them. This is not intolerable so long as science puts to itself the Eleatic question, but if it asks, How are actual changes brought about, accepting change and multiplicity as facts, then the whole rational structure of modern science becomes irrelevant in spite of its prestige. M. Myerson seems to believe that this is inevitable. " Le mécanisme et son aboutissement ultime, la réduction de la réalité au néant, font partie intégrante de la science: c'est que celle-ci, en effet, ne saurait se soustraire à la domination du principe d'identité, qui est la forme essentielle de notre pensée." (*IR* 287). But after all why must we think thus when we see the absurdity of the situation? We are clearly aware—thanks to M. Meyerson—that the trouble lies in clinging to the principle of identity. Why can we not then abandon this principle?

Science itself in fact does not absorb the principle completely. The second law of thermodynamics, as M. Meyerson points out, refuses to lend itself to eleaticism, and both transitive action and sensory qualities remain as " irrationals." These, as we shall see, are doomed to escape explanation forever—and yet they are the distinguishing marks of the world with which science starts.[23]

[23] The second law is again discussed in *ES* 204 ff.

V

The second law of thermodynamics has this peculiarity, that it states a tendency of nature towards a future condition. Thus it proposes a direction for natural processes rather than a static reversibility. This marks its difference from the usual scientific principles; they can be expressed as equations (*IR* 296) whereas the increase of entropy cannot. For this reason it is not "plausible,"[24] and scientists have persistently tried to explain it away or to escape its consequences. M. Meyerson (*IR* 302) notes several of these attempts, such as those of Haeckel and Arrhenius, or theories about the reconcentration of the sun's lost energy such as that of Rankine (*IR* 303), or escapes through the liberation of intra-atomic energy (*IR* 308), or Boltzmann's theory of *æons* in which the sum of entropy would increase only in relatively small periods (*IR* 309). These can all be shown to be unsatisfactory for reasons clearly expounded by M. Meyerson. We might add to them the attempt to escape through statistics.[25] According, to this, the Carnot-Clausius principle is indeed the most probable but there is a very slight—yet finite—probability that the sum of entropy decreases.

[24] It is well to recall what "plausibility" means. "Toute proposition stipulant identité dans le temps, toute loi de conservation est plausible" (*IR* 162).

[25] Cf. the discussion of the statistical treatment of thermodynamics in *ES* 206 ff.

Therefore, it is argued,[26] the concentration rather than the dissipation of energy is not impossible. Nevertheless although it is not in one sense of the word impossible, if we are to use statistics in physics, " impossible " must mean " the very highly improbable," [27] and with the probability of a decrease in entropy so slight, it amounts to a statistical inconceivability. We should like therefore to add this to M. Meyerson's list of failures to explain away the direction to the world.

The fundamentality of the Carnot-Clausius principle to all physical change shows us how illusory the " equals " sign is as a representation of phenomena (*IR* 319). For if the equation symbolizes change and the change is real or physical, it is self-evident that the process is not reversible, for change requires energy and the energy is inevitably dissipated (*IR* 321). This would only be avoided if the two sides of the equation were interchangeable and we know that they are not, for each equation represents an operation. Only the science which analyses and presents its analyses in the form of " explanations " uses identity; empirical science is bound to reintroduce change into the world (*IR* 323). The Carnot-Clausius principle shows that reversibility is purely ideal and that time cannot be eliminated in any de-

[26] For a popular exposition of this point of view, see G. N. Lewis's *The Anatomy of Science,* New Haven, 1926, ch. VI, esp. pp. 141 *et seq.*

[27] Cf. Haas's *The New Physics,* N. Y., 1923 (?), p. 39. Cf. *ES* 212.

scription of the real. It expresses nature's resistance to the restraints put upon her by our understanding (*IR* 326).

But if this be true, the inquiring reader is bound to ask, Are there two kinds of science, one ideal and one empirical? Is ideal science an analysis of phenomena, an attempt to define in what Descartes would have called the geometrical fashion the more complex ideas by the simpler? Is it only this science which uses the principle of identity, of enduring substances which " explain " change by denying it? Is it ideal science to which we are indebted for the *êtres fictifs* upon which the structure of the universe depends? If so—and it would seem so—we may well ask what the relationship of ideal science is to empirical science and what claim it has to truth.

It is self-evident that one could not deduce the existence of change from postulates which denied its existence and hence if, as M. Meyerson has pointed out with admirable skill, ideal science derives its existence from the denial of change, it is certain that empirical science cannot logically be deduced from it. There is just as great a break between the two as between the two worlds of Plato and a break of exactly the same sort, for what makes the difference is not a property which admits of degrees but one which is absolute.[28] The technique which produces ideal sci-

[28] Neo-Platonism tried to weld this break together by the theory of emanations—for which there was no evidence whatsoever, except an intellectual need for a welding of some sort—and we know how little satisfactory the theory was.

ence is helpless in dealing with empirical science, helpless because the world of experience has, to repeat, as its essential trait a property whose existence is denied by ideal science.

The question again stubbornly puts itself why we must remain faithful to ideal science if this be the situation. If the understanding is so clearly shown to be impotent in dealing with experience, why must we continue in the Eleatic path of denying experience to the profit of the reason? Before attempting to answer this inevitable question, let us continue M. Meyerson's account of the inadequacy of the reason.

Not only then can it not admit the existence of change (and time) but it has to deny the existence of qualities (sensations) or treat them as negligible (*IR* 325). Its world is a world of colliding billiard balls; the world of experience is a world of qualities. Two particles of matter in collision may cause the appearance of a sensation—a color or a sound, for instance—but by no stretch of the imagination can the color or the sound be said to exist in the particles of matter. Hence the most science can do is to accept their existence as a fact, and resign itself to not explaining them.

Similarly the manner in which two impacting bodies act upon one another is bound to be an irrational (*IR* 338). Such impact is essential to mechanism. Without impact (*le choc*) all mechanical action would cease (*IR* 339). Yet what is transferred in impact? Not motion. For the motion is the relation of a body to other bodies or to spatial or spatio-temporal co-ordinates,[29] and hence it cannot be transferred from one body to another. One body may move to a point " contiguous " to another and the other may then move off. But how or why it moves off is bound to be inexplicable. Thus mechanical action exists as a law but can never be called a deduction. This, as M. Meyerson has pointed out with his customary historical erudition, was noticed as early as the fourteenth century by Holkot (*IR* 342).[30]

Even when we locate transitive action in the tangible world of sensory experience, it remains stubbornly inexplicable. The contacts which occur can never be other than the contiguity of two discrete sensa (*IR* 349) and anything transitive within this contiguity is bound to be read into it and not observed. We can see one billiard ball approach and

[29] I depart from M. Meyerson's expressions here, see *IR* 340 f. "Il ne saurait y avoir de mouvement sans substrat matériel, sans quelque chose qui se meut. Le mouvement n'a rien d'une substance, et c'est tout au plus si nous pouvons le considérer comme un *état*. A supposer que nous acceptions ce dernier concept, que nous considérions que cet état doive durer indéfiniment, ainsi que l'exige le principe d'inertie, comment pourrait-il se détacher d'un corps pour s'attacher à un autre? Il faudrait, comme l'a très justement remarqué Lotze, qu'entre les deux cet état existât un moment (infiniment court si l'on veut) en soi, comme une véritable substance, ce qui est absurde. Mais il n'est pas possible de supposer que cette transmission n'exige qu'un espace de temps infiniment court. Tout, dans la nature, se passe dans le temps, et admettre que quelque chose puisse se produire en dehors de lui, c'est concéder que le cours de l'univers entier n'est plus conditionné par le temps."

[30] Cf. *ES* app. I on the precursors of Hume.

touch another; we cannot see it send the other flying. We can see the ax touch the tree; we cannot see it chop it down. The " activity " of these verbs is theory, interpretation; it is not observation and by its very nature cannot be.

This gives us three irrationals: change, sensory qualities, impact. To them we shall add a fourth, suggested by M. Meyerson's treatment of evolutionism (*IR* 357). Evolutionism—which of course need not be biological—rests upon the discovery or postulation of histories, or " courses of events." Their patterns may differ, but that the event moves in a certain direction, has a beginning, a middle, and an end, is a distinctive property. There is of course a whole group of intellectual disciplines whose data are courses of events and we may lump them together under the name of " the historical sciences." It has frequently been pointed out, especially in recent times, that analysis tells you very little of what occurs in history. It may unravel the various strands which are interwoven but can tell you no more about its course than a lateral cross section of a river can tell you about a river's course. The history is a unit but a temporal unit and hence its internal progression is so intimate a part of it that to deny it is to denature it. The historical sciences therefore cannot be mechanical nor can they be " explanatory " in the Meyersonian sense of the word. M. Meyerson would deny that they were more than inchoate sciences and hence feels freer than the present writer does to ignore them. Nevertheless they are growing rather than decreasing and whenever they have oriented themselves towards mechanism (see section II of this essay), they have become proportionately unsatisfactory, as is attested by the rapidity with which mechanistic histories have been dropped.

Change itself is the stuff upon which science feeds; without it science would be uncalled for. Sensory qualities are our only evidence of the existence of a world. Transitive action is utilized by science to explain the changes whose existence it admits even without explaining. History is incorporate in at least half of the phenomena which constitute our world. If now science is incapable of interpreting these four admittedly real traits of the world, why is it our duty to give it our continued reverence, especially when we know where the root of the difficulty lies? It may be replied that science has never used any other technique. And indeed M. Meyerson has shown that both non-mechanical theories and common sense alike rest on a base of causalism. Nevertheless—apart from common sense—reason has no desire to falsify experience and as soon as it appreciates what it has done, it will take another path.

For the historical sciences show that the causalistic metaphysics is not absolutely necessary and everyone admits that a legalistic science is at least the first (if not the last) step towards a rational interpretation of the world. The great question, however, that will arise is what the laws are true of. If one says, of *things,* the metaphysics of the thing immediately rises to torment one. The thing, however, is a concept generated by causalism (See *IR,* ch XI) and one cannot avoid its paradoxes by unconsciously reasserting them. We have then apparently the way open either towards phenomenalism—which certainly has too many undesirable traits to be considered a likely choice—or towards " objective relativism " in one form or another. Whether these be the only possibilities or not, we shall not here discuss. But certainly it is evident that some choice must be made if science is to give a more recognizable picture of the world. Its problem is to admit the reality of time and change (perhaps even to posit them as basic rather than identity and unity). Why things change then could not be so great a problem as why they persist. Is this answering a problem by denying that it is a problem? In part. But no more so than the way of causalism, for that attitude, finding itself impotent to handle change, denies that change exists. One is faced either with accepting a fact as a fact and not as a problem or with denying the existence of a fact.

This seems the natural conclusion to be drawn from *Identité et Réalité.* Nevertheless, there is no reason to suppose that scientists will draw this conclusion. Most of them are confirmed positivists in theory anyway, though confirmed causalists in practice.[31] Moreover, one can adopt the attitude of

[31] See *ES,* ch. I.

M. Meyerson himself which is to rest content with what science has done in the past without pretending to guess or dictate its future course. "When science reforms, then we can talk about it," may be the beginning of wisdom. Yet it may be excusable, if somewhat presumptuous, to point out the need of reform.

PART TWO

De l'Explication dans les Sciences

The question that naturally faces the scientist of a critical turn of mind is whether, if he is a " legalist," he can find a subject matter for his laws. Before the possibility of " objective relativism " occurred to philosophers, the only possible subject matters were " things " or " sensations " (phenomena) and legalists such as Comte appear to choose the latter alternative. This choice is most consistently adhered to in Mach and his influence upon scientists has probably been more telling than that of the founder of positivism himself. If we disregard the third possibility, indicated by " objective relativism," we find it necessary to enquire whether in fact science can be phenomenalistic or whether on the contrary it has not been persistently ontological. The first chapter of *De l'Explication dans les Sciences* pursues this inquiry.

M. Meyerson in this chapter attempts to demonstrate that science cannot exist without " things," that when none are observed it imagines them, and that even the most ostensibly positivistic branches of science—such as thermodynamics—presuppose the existence of realities independent of the observer.

According to positivism, he declares (*ES* 20), science seeks a knowledge of *relations* only and has no interest in the nature of their terms. This is fortified by a quotation from Comte, " Toute hypothèse physique, afin d'être réellement jugeable, doit exclusivement porter sur les lois des phenomènes et jamais sur leur mode de production." (*Ib.*) This would seem to imply that the laws of nature can be known independently of nature; that we can know the relationship between *A* and *B* without knowing *A* and *B*. And indeed there is a metaphysics of that sort which erects scientific laws—as Plato erected common natures—into self-dependent entities which form a quasi-mathematical world into which the proper initiation gives us entrance. We have no doubt a tendency to hypostatize whatever we talk of, since we give it a name and names seem to denote " things," and even π and other functions are spoken of as " things."

Nevertheless there are reasons to believe that the laws of nature are not so much descriptions of how nature behaves as of how we observe nature. We have, for instance (*ES* 22), the firm conviction that nature is mathematical and we feel that the most perfect laws are those which are in mathematical form. But mathematical form is itself the result of years of historical development. " Ainsi, en formulant la loi de la réfraction, nous nous servons de la fonction du sinus, qui nous paraît toute simple, parce qu'elle nous est familière et que nous possédons même des tables nous permettant d'en déterminer rapidement la valeur. Mais si nous devions l'exprimer à l'aide de séries, elle nous apparaîtrait, au contraire, comme assez compliquée et nous donnerions au rapport en question une expression tout autre " (*ES* 22). But within mathematics itself, to add a suggestion of our own, our definitions and laws betray the same human traits. It is only of recent years that Euclidean geometry—the earliest branch of mathematics to be codified—has been purged of its intuitional elements. " A straight line is the shortest distance between two points " contains little of purely geometrical interest. Are we to say that " modern " Euclidean geometry is more true to nature than ancient? We can simply maintain that it is more elegant. But since when have we been assured that elegance is a criterion of truth? One might ask whether a circle is " really " " a regular plane polygon with an infinite number of sides," or " a plane figure all the points on whose perimeter are equidistant from another point called the center," or " the figure described by a straight line continuously moving about one of its end points in a plane." Such a question is obviously childish, just as questions about the " real " formula for the parallel postulate would be childish.

If one should now attempt to save the objectivity of laws by abandoning their mathematical form, one would find himself making a barren sacrifice (*ES* 23). In support of this M. Meyerson asks what would be the nature of a chemical element, say " sulfur," as used in a chemical law? The chemist certainly does not mean this or that particular particle of yellow matter. He means, on the contrary, an ideal sulphur whose properties he will probably never meet. This he calls his "chemically pure" substance. But these chemically pure substances exist only in books; they are "êtres créés par des théories" (*Ib.*); they are *genera* in the Scholastic sense of the word and, we may add, mathematical limits which we may approach in our observations but never reach. We must indeed be prepared for their senescence: they may go the way of the four elements of Empedocles which survived almost until the nineteenth century. Already in fact we see signs of their approaching death. Since we have adopted atomic weights as differentiating characteristics, we have found that certain elements, such as lead and chlorine, have a variety of atomic weights, although chemically they are identical. Are we to say that they are not "really" the same element or that a given element may be heterogeneous? As is well know, we have concluded that these specimens should be given the name of "isotopes." But they are isotopes *of lead* or *of chlorine.* But in practise this can mean little more than that a group of substances of similar but not identical weights react to certain tests identically. Which destroys the value of the pigeon holes of the periodic law as means of partitioning the elements and suggests that "chlorine" and "lead" are the names for a group of substances having related atomic weights. They become exactly analogous to the names of biological species. But if this be true, why set such store by chemical purity? Is there a biologically pure horse or primrose?

The chemically pure element is paralleled in physics by the " ideal gas " (*ES* 26). " Jamais nous ne rencontrerons dans la nature le ' gaz idéal ' de la théorie, ni les cristaux tels que nous les montrent les modèles cristallographiques. Tout cela n'est que généralisation, abstraction, chose de notre pensée, *idée* dans le sens platonicien du terme." (*Ib.*) The ideal gas like the chemically pure element is a child of theory. To believe in their real existence is to revive the theory of medieval realism (*ES* 28) and thereby to raise the more than vexatious problem of the relation of this world of logical reals to the world of perceived particulars. We know that our particulars approximate the laws in their behaviour. " Les lois formulées par nous ne peuvent être qu'une image de l'ordonnance réelle de la nature, elles ne lui correspondent que dans la mesure où une projection peut correspondre à un corps à *n* dimensions, elles ne l'expriment qu'autant qu'un mot écrit exprime la chose, car, dans les deux cas, il faut passer par l'intermédiaire de notre entendement. La loi particulière n'existait pas, au sens le plus littéral du terme, avant d'avoir été formulée, et elle cessera d'exister le jour où elle sera fondue dans une loi plus générale. Et qu'on le remarque bien, très souvent la loi disparaîtra non pas parce qu'elle constituera dorénavant le cas particulier d'une règle plus générale, mais parce qu'elle se trouvera véritablement abolie, et qu'elle sera reconnue comme n'étant qu'une première et grossière approximation, démentie par des déterminations plus précises. Depuis la loi de Newton, nous savons que les lois de Képler ne peuvent être exactes qu'à peu près, et la théorie cinétique nous enseigne qu'aucun gaz ne peut rigoureusement suivre la loi de Mariotte." (*ES* 29)

Thus we can be assured that our laws are not really laws of nature but the laws of nature in its relation to our sensation and intelligence (*ES* 30). We can, moreover, only know the relations between things, but even then these relations must include ourselves as a third term. They are, one might say triadic instead of dyadic and the observer must be figured in.

Is this merely a reassertion of the ego-centric predicament? (We are leaving M. Meyerson for the moment.) Are we simply arguing that " we can only know the world as known " ? Not at all. That phrasing of the ego-centric predicament does not account for the fact that we can detect our presence knowing. Just as we can detect the personal equation by the comparison of one observer's results with another's, so we can detect the human equation or the instrumental equation either by comparing our results with those of other animals or by comparing the results of different instruments. If nothing else existed, we could utilize the conclusions of the special theory of relativity to show us how far the " point of view " of the observer enters into his conception of the world, and we know how strange a world resulted in the general theory when an attempt was made to eliminate the difficulties of individual points of view. Yet that world was no different in essence from the world of Euclidean geometry, in which also the individual point of view is eliminated. A person confined to visual perspectives would have a hard time reconciling his various shapes with the solid figure called a cube and it is indeed doubtful whether the latter could ever be logically constructed out of the former. Hence natural laws do not depict for us the nature of things apart from their behaviour nor do they seem to exist apart from us. Are they, however, as positivism thinks (*ES* 31), rules governing the whole of our sensations? It is true that Comte himself did not see the strict equivalence between positivism and phenomenalism,[1] though Mill was more clear-sighted. For Mill, to whom, it will be remembered, matter was but the permanent possibility of sensations, the laws of science could denote nothing other than our immediate experiences and their inter-relations. This is a logical implication of positivism, M. Meyerson believes (*ES* 32), since the prohibition of explanation, of seeking what produces the sensation, leaves only the sensation itself as the subject matter of science. The world of " things " is constructed out of our need for an explanation of our sensations. Were this need not felt, we should rest

[1] But see important footnote, *ES* 31, n. 1.

content with the sensations themselves. But they would be none too easy to find. Following the lead of M. Bergson, M. Meyerson points out that " the immediate data of consciousness " are only with great difficulty extricated from the perceptual matrix in which they occur. Hence were a positivistic (i. e., a phenomenalistic) science to be constructed—and it is by no means certain that it could be—it would be a sort of psychophysics, entirely different from the science to which we are accustomed.

Yet, as *advocatus diaboli* (or *diabolorum*) we must suggest that whether one penetrate to the *données immédiates* or not, is of small moment. These data are themselves no more " elementary " than the percepts in which they occur or which they are supposed to constitute. We have recently learned from the Gestalt-psychology [2] that they are, on the contrary, functions of the " introspective attitude " and hence have no more claim to genetic priority than the percepts—or physical objects of common sense. That analysis is possible proves that there is such a physical object—whether " subjective " or " objective " does not concern us here—a point at which the analysis can start, and the probability is that it is much more stable and enduring than the immediate data which come into existence only in psychological laboratories under the very special conditions familiar to readers of the literature. Science can then deal with such beings and their inter-relations and it is

[2] Köhler's *Gestalt Psychology,* N. Y. 1929, ch. III.

certain that biological science at least does. A zoologist never dreams of substituting either his sensations or infra-perceptual realities—atoms, molecules, etc.—for what lies before his eyes. They have, therefor, enough stability and objectivity for legalistic purposes and, as a matter of fact, most of the *êtres fictifs* of the physical sciences are patterned after them, at least in their visual and tactual aspects. It may be true that, as Malebranche has argued (*ES* 33), the sensations cannot be measured and compared among themselves; but the percepts may, for we do it every time we apply a yard stick or use a pair of scales. We may be simply substituting one *gestalt* for another, but whatever the explanation, we have something here which lends itself to scientific treatment and mathematical calculations.

But this involves the deeper question of whether the Meyersonian distinction between an entity's " nature " and its " behaviour " (or " relations ") is fundamentally sound. It is certainly true that the distinction is made in common sense. We say that natures are revealed in behaviour. Thus a sanguine temperament—to take an old fashioned example—is revealed in flushed cheeks, gaiety of manner, embonpoint, and so on. The acidity of a given substance is revealed in its reaction to litmus paper tests and the like, the flow of electricity by a galvanometer, the pressure of the atmosphere by the height of a column of mercury in a barometer. But we should feel disinclined to say that the sanguine temperament is flushed cheeks, etc., that the acidity is the turning of the blue litmus paper red, that the flow of electricity is the movement of the indicator on a galvanometer, that atmospheric pressure is the height of a column of mercury. At most the general run of us maintain that these tests are effects produced by the " nature " in question and only by that nature. That is why they are good tests.

And yet if we are to ask what the " nature " is in addition to the concentration of a group of such tests at a certain region of space, it is doubtful whether any satisfactory answer can be given. " Doubtful," I say, for there may be a satisfactory answer which has not so far been discovered. Whatever answer is given will, to be intelligible, be necessarily in terms of observation—either direct (as in the case of seeing a color) or indirect (as in " observing " certain invisible waves). In the former case the " nature " of the color is whatever it happens to be, which is of course ineffable until linked by memory to other similar experiences and correlated with other people's experience in social intercourse. The elaborate technique of separating it out from the complex in which it occurs, of seeing it as a single entity, of relating it to other experiences, we need not elaborate. Once established as a given color—red—it is the color red and its nature is settled. But most of the things which science discusses are not thus directly seized. They are grasped indirectly by means of percepts and sensa which are presumably their effects or elaborate mathematical and pseudo-mathematical concepts. We no more know their " natures " apart from tests of their presence than our fathers in the seventeenth and eighteenth centuries knew substances apart from qualities. Substance, it will be recalled, evolved into the unknown things-in-themselves of Kant, which were soon relegated into an eternal limbo. Is that not bound to be the fate of entities which cannot be empirically known? Whatever will be said about the things in the universe will inevitably take the form of statements about their behaviour. Hence one is almost irresistibly driven to the conclusion that the " nature " of *X* is " to behave in such and such a specific observable fashion." [3]

It seems then that the agglomeration of behaviour-strands into " things " results from a judicious selection of a system of reference. To return to our isotopes again, is Isotope I the same element as Isotope II or are they different? Is it not largely a matter of history that we should speak of isotopes " of the same element " rather than of the identical chemical behaviour of certain different elements? Why, that is, are the tests of atomic weight less of a differentiating property than the tests utilized in chemical reactions? As a matter of fact, the periodic law was constructed on the basis of pigeon-holing

[3] I state this with a certain reluctance, for I should prefer to have natures and behaviours separable. But I have as yet found no way to keep them so.

the elements according to their atomic weights, for it was believed that atomic weights were a kind of finger print which would infallibly identify the various elements. According to that basic hypothesis it would be more fitting to give each isotope a different name, just as sodium and potassium are given different names in spite of the similarity of certain of their chemical properties. The whole matter, however, is solved by permitting two things to be one in one system of relations and two in another, and the problem becomes simply one of nomenclature.

In that case the reactions of a groups of *X's* to one set of tests will be called the " nature " of *X* and *X* will be given a name denoting that group of reactions and sometimes derived from it.[4] It will then be assumed that all the *X's* ought to react identically—or nearly so—to all other tests. If they do, then these tests will be the behaviour of *X* rather than its nature. If they do not, then *X* will be said to have varieties, or phases, or sub-groups, and the like, which behave differently.

But now if, as we believe, the distinction between nature and behaviour fades away in practice and natures are revealed only in behaviour, then it is clear that only the relations of things can be studied and that the positing of an *X* is useful only to satisfy the need of having a term for our relations. That raises the question of whether we are not suffering from devotion to linguistics rather than experience,

[4] Cf. " oxygen," " hydrogen."

as in so-called " dialectical " reasoning. May we not be forced to the unpleasant conclusion that the distinction between terms and relations is as useless as the distinction between subject and property and that we need a new vocabulary to denote the events which are occurring in the world?

It does not seem to the present writer that a positivistic science need be phenomenalistic unless we have previously demonstrated that the physical objects of common sense are groups of *données immédiates*. Yet we can continue with M. Meyerson in pointing out that the physical scientist certainly does not believe that he is studying his sensations (*ES* 33). It is undoubtedly true [5] that science has moved farther and farther away from sensation or from whatever involves an observer. It is also true that no one has as yet succeeded in erecting a science which simply correlates sensations and, we may I think add, no one has tried to. " Au contraire, chaque phrase, chaque affirmation, si on l'examnie, témoignera d'une foi inébranlable dans l'existence de choses, dans leur indépendence de la sensation." But again what are these *things*, other than a constellation of invariable properties, properties like the tertiary qualities of Locke? It is certain that no scientist—except in his philosophical moments—ever thought that these constellations were " subjective " nor does the logic of his position drive him to such a thought.

[5] In fact we should never venture to dispute any of M. Meyerson's historical conclusions, though we do not always draw the same inferences from them.

It is undeniable that the laws of physics are supposed (and justly) to apply to extra-subjective entities. But that these entities have no empirical counterparts, make no difference to sensation, is as incredible as that they have the same ontological status as dreams and phantasms.

Thus the physicist, when he has no common sense things, creates others in their image (*ES* 38). Such are telescopic and microscopic objects, as well as the "scientific objects," molecules, atoms, electrons, and protons, whose existence is *simplement inférée* (*Ib.*). If one hid a galvanometer behind a screen, the electrician would not believe that the current whose presence it revealed had ceased to flow. For he believes that he is studying not the motions of a galvanometric indicator but the flow of an electric current. Yet one might ask whether, if there were no way of observing the galvanometer or if the inferred electric current "made no difference" to observation, the physicist would have any reason to believe in the existence of an electric current. The answer to that question is inevitably negative, as is proved by the history of electric-theory. It arose entirely from certain peculiar sensory observations which seemed *sui generis* and turned out to be so and it took its original and subsequent forms from the peculiarities of those observations.[6]

[6] To say nothing of the observations, more or less random, of Theoprastus and Pliny, we find Gilbert himself beginning with the observable peculiarities of amber and the lodestone. The article, *Electricity,* in the *Encyclopedia Britannica* (11th ed.), tells the tale

It is now time to ask what constitutes a "thing." "Ce qui constitue la chose, c'est le fait d'être indépendant de la sensation: la chose reste ce qu'elle est, que je la regarde ou non" (*ES* 40). But only things especially constructed by the imagination to be thus invariant to observation can ever be discovered or inferred to exist, for the simple reason that whatever is directly observed is in part at least sensory—or imaginal which comes to the same thing. Hence the "qualities" of things can never be discovered or even imagined and when one tries to, one makes obvious errors which do not deceive even the imaginer. What one can discover or infer is their relation to observation, which is usually—probably always—causal. Therefore in what sense of the word are "things" independent of sensation? They would never be posited at all were it not for the variability of sensation, which is first stabilized into the physical object of common sense and then, when the physical object proves equally unsatisfactory, is refined into the "scientific object." Should the (presumably) same scientific object give rise to two diverse sensations, it is clear that the scientist would deny its sameness, unless he were able to preserve it by attributing the sensory diversity to the conditions of observation. Hence even in believing in the inde-

with sufficient illustrations for our purpose. See Vol. IX, 180 B. To be sure, no science could be built up from observations in the sense of sense-data, or essences, detached from everything else, inasmuch as they are by hypothesis inarticulable. It is the total observable *gestalt* which I mean by "the object of observation."

pendent " thing," the scientist is discussing its relations, and although he may endow it with eleatic properties, he can discuss it only in relation to heraclitan experience. Even when he is postulating absolute constants, such as energy, physical mass, the atoms, and electrons, he knows perfectly well that their constancy creates as many problems as it solves and serves rather to pacify his hunger for absolutes than to explain the diverse occurrences of the observed world. For having made his mass absolute—we are remaining in the field of pre-Einsteinian physics—he then has the problem of measuring it, and its measure will always be relative to the instruments and means of measurement chosen. Having determined upon the absoluteness of energy—which as M. Meyerson himself has shown is a reified integral—he finds the problem of its apparent appearance and disappearance on his hands and invents the complementary " thing," potential energy. The history of the atoms and electrons similarly illustrates the dependence of things upon observation and although the scientist may believe in their independence, so does he also frequently believe in positivism and with no better right. Just, as M. Meyerson has shown, he may believe in one methodology while employing another, so he may believe in the independence of his " things " while treating them as relations.

That some ontology will arise we can accept wholeheartedly. It is certain that the human reason is metaphysical (*ES* 43) and anti-phenomenalistic. But whether the metaphysics which it inevitably reaches is that of absolute things with relative properties is still an open question. Nevertheless up to the writing of M. Meyerson's first two books, the overwhelming tendency of the scientist was to postulate such a metaphysics and our only legitimate question is whether his results made sense.

The first chapter of *De l'Explication dans les Sciences,* then, attempts to demonstrate how thought demands the existence of things independent of human thought. The second points out how science passes beyond description to explanation, and in fact creates and seeks things for the sole purpose of explanation.

The fundamental error of positivism, according to M. Meyerson (*ES* 45), is in believing that science has the unique goal of action. This was the error which lay at the root of the Baconian philosophy and which continued through the Enlightenment until it grew into a rounded out theory in Comte. Opposed to it is the theory that science exists for " understanding," that the application of science to " life " was accidental and not essential. If the utilitarian view has the support of the social reformers, the theoretical view—if the verbal redundancy is pardonable—has the support of Plato, Aristotle, Montaigne, Pascal, and lesser names (*ES* 46). Comte denied the importance of the desire for pure knowledge, as could be predicted, but nevertheless had to admit its existence and the greater number of scientists maintain that its satisfaction is their sole aim.

That science is not satisfied by description, however minute and detailed, is attested by the discussion aroused by the Newtonian law of gravitation. Newton left it as a description, as a mathematical formula which stated how gravitation worked. Nothing could have been simpler or more precise, provided one understood the meaning of the symbols. And yet the law was no sooner published than attempts were made to *explain* the phenomena it so clearly described (*IR* 46, and *App.* I; *ES* 48). What was this force of attraction which pulled masses towards each other? Was it material or immaterial? Was it " essential and inherent to matter " or externally derived? If law was sufficient, why should such questions have arisen?

At the other end of science, in biology, a similar situation arose, in the split between mechanists and finalists. The former hope to explain all behaviour in terms of physics, the latter insist on introducing " ends "; but both agree that empirical description does not suffice to explain phenomena (*ES* 49). If it did, there would be no reason to ask why the animal acts as it does, or why the organ functions as it does. A simple description of what the organ does would be sufficient. But we might add here a word of our own that a " simple description " is impossible in the biological sciences, even if realizable in the physical. The simplest description of the functions of the heart inevitably locates the heart in its milieu which is the entire system of veins and arteries. One could lop it off and simply count its beats, but in that case it would be like cutting a pump out of a pumping system and describing it as such and such a mass moving vertically up and down a shaft. To locate an organ in its proper milieu involves no decision between the merits of mechanism and vitalism; all biologists are bound to agree that the heart does something for the general economy of the body. Whether it is as it is because of the purpose or whether it has that purpose because of what it is seems like a significant issue—though one may permissibly doubt whether it really is or not—but to recognize a physiological purpose is no less descriptive than to recognize that the earth goes round the sun. That too may be described teleologically and has been. In fact one could debate why it goes round the sun in the same spirit as one debates why the heart functions. Is the "why" of the scientist that kind of "why"?

The same demand for explanation which lies beneath description, voiced by astronomers and biologists, is also voiced by physical chemists. M. Meyerson cites the discussions that arose in the Solvay Congress of 1911 among whose members were H. Poincaré, Brillouin, Lorentz, Planck, Rutherford, and others of similar mark (*ES* 51). This congress was seeking not a description—for it had descriptions—but an explanation of a whole series of phenomena which contradicted all the theories formulated to date. The discussion centered about Planck's quantum-hypothesis and the difficulty of harmonizing it with the classical laws of electrodynamics. Even Einstein insisted on the necessity of a " concrete " presentation of the theory which would explain " why an electron in a metal hit by Roentgen rays takes on the great kinetic energy observed for the secondary cathode rays? All the metal is in the field of the Roentgen rays. Why does only a small portion of the electrons take on this velocity of cathode rays? Whence does it come about that the energy is absorbed only at very few points? " (*ES* 52). This obviously is reasoning from a mechanical model—imaginary to be sure—of all the metal's electrons spread out before the Roentgen rays which, instead of affecting the whole field uniformly, affect only certain parts of it—and those very few in number; as if a spray of water aimed at a square board should dampen only a few spots distributed not over the whole square. This must be explained and the explanation must be a *concrete reality.* Nevertheless, in spite of the Congress's labors—and the most eminent scientists partook in them—no such concrete reality was found and the question is as much disputed in 1929 as it was eighteen years before. Yet no one, according to M. Meyerson (*ES* 54), has said that the search must be abandoned and Planck himself rejected the suggestion of Lamor and Debye which was to treat the whole matter phenomenalistically.

It is only fair to note that since that time the question has been debated more and more from the point of view of statistics. When one remains content with equations of probability, one has abandoned any hope of Meyersonian explanation. This is usually expressed as probability's being the measure of our ignorance. That is, of course, hardly accurate enough even for an epigram, for probability is no more subjective than certainty and all scientific laws measure our ignorance, since they are based upon human observations rather than divine revelations. Nevertheless it renounces any attempt to explain why one thing happens rather than another. This is apparent even in the simplest cases. When we remark that in tossing a coin there is an even chance of obtaining heads or tails, we abandon any attempt to explain why heads turns up rather than tails. It is true that we often add that if we knew enough we could tell which would turn up. But how much would be enough? The answer is obvious and shows us that we may as well rest with that amount of knowledge which permits us to calculate our probabilities. In the case of coins each toss is an individual event and individual events within limits are by their very nature capable of doing anything, nor is it possible to predict those elements which make them individual. The limits of their capabilities are defined by their similarity to other events. This is recognized in the construction of games of chance: if one were to make one of the compartments on a roulette wheel larger than the others, the probability of the ball's rolling into any compartment is changed. If, therefore, we have enough data to calculate the distribution of the velocity of the cathode rays, what more could one legitimately demand?

Be that as it may, M. Meyerson with his usual historical erudition points out that no one pursued this course and all on the contrary went on demanding a causal explanation. And if we are to judge the future by the past, they will go on seeking a causal explanation and will abandon statistics when they have found one. They will be no more satisfied by positivistic formulæ in science than we are in the realm of legerdemain (*ES* 56). For explanation gives us a familiar type of inner satisfaction. "Chacun peut en faire directement l'expérience sur lui-même, en s'initiant à une théorie mécanique qu'il ignorait précédemment; si cette théorie est peu ou prou adaptée aux faits, il aura certainement le sentiment de comprendre le *pourquoi* des faits en question. De grands savants, sans aucun parti pris antipositiviste, par simple souci de préciser leur méthode, l'ont constaté: 'Si je puis faire un modèle mécanique, dit Kelvin, je comprends; si je ne peux pas en faire un, je ne comprends pas.'—et l'évolution tout entière de la science confirme cette assertion. Il suffit, en effet, d'ouvrir un manuel quelconque, à n'importe quel chapitre, pour se convaincre que la science est remplie de ces théories explicatives, et il n'est pas besoin de pénétrer bien profondément dans l'histoire de la pensée scientifique pour constater qu'il en a été ainsi à toutes les époques, que jamais il n'a existé quoi que ce fût méritant véritablement le nom de science et ressemblant de près ou de loin au schéma positiviste" (*ES* 57). Therefore explicative science exists as a fact in spite of Comte's efforts (and those of Hegel, too, as M. Meyerson shows) to denounce it. Law plays a large rôle in science, permitting us as it does both prediction and action, but it does not satisfy our minds.

It is for the sake of explanation that science seeks things. It can have its laws without them but when it asks, as it inevitably does, *why* the law is so and so, it must have things. They alone provide that basis of unalterable identity on which science insists. And though they at the end of the story may have characters which phenomena do not have, it is they which science will hold to be real and not phenomena.

II

Science then constructs its things for the sake of explanation and we must now ask when an explanation will be satisfactory. The second book of *De l'Explication dans les Sciences* seeks an answer to that question.

By "explanation" the scientist means "causal explanation," and when he has ascertained the cause of an event, he will be satisfied. "Cause" in common sense connotes a temporal *anteriority* to the phenomenon known as the effect (*ES* 65). It also connotes a *necessary* connection between the two terms so that they imply one another (*ES* 66). It is sometimes synonymous with " reason " or " sufficient reason " and a reason is held to be sufficient when it produces the effect. But a reason cannot produce anything in the world which lies beyond the reason and hence the causal series will be that rational series known as deduction. " La cause, dès lors, peut se définir comme le point de départ d'une déduction dont le phénomène sera le point d'aboutissement " (*Ib.*). When such a deduction is made, our reason is satisfied and though it may ask the cause of the cause or the effect of the effect, it will no longer struggle to explain the cause of the effect.

When now we relate the formulation of causality to the etymological meaning of *explication,* we find that in order to explicate what is implicit, the effect must pre-exist in the cause and there must be an identity between the two.[7] Therefore explanation is a process of showing that the effect is a logical consequence of its cause or causes and it presupposes that the whole world can be so envisaged that its phe-

[7] Yet compare the phenomenon legalized in the law of the parallelogram of forces. The direction which ensues from the collision of two moving particles is a vector of the two directions and thus can be deduced from them and is, of course, " conditioned " or, if one wishes, " caused " by them. But in what sense of the word does it pre-exist in them? Though it is spoken of as their product, this leads no one to believe that it was " in " them in the sense that a coin is in a purse or a plant (metaphorically) in a seed. We might add that we have yet to find a case of causation *in the world of observation* which could not be described in terms of vectors, better than in terms of pre-existence.

nomena contain nothing absurd or discordant with our reason. Thus understanding makes the succession of phenomena seem necessary rather than contingent, as Spinoza put it in a now classical phrase (*ES* 68).

Let us halt for a moment to consider the concept " necessity." A single event selected out of the universe by the imagination may be considered to be either acting according to necessity or free will or absolute arbitrariness, as one likes. For to state that *X* is contingent is to relate it to not-*X*—i. e., those things upon which it is contingent—and not-*X* is by hypothesis excluded from our discussion. Hence its path—if it could have a path—could be noted but one would be forced to say, " It acts thus and so because that is its nature." In logic and mathematics (and mathematical physics) we are treating of such entities, for the " universals " whose inter-relations one discusses follow exactly the same rules as individuals. We are dealing (this is an old story) with " circularity " not circles, universal-affirmativeness-of-propositions, not this or that universal affirmative proposition, and it is only insofar as the real world of particulars can be made to fit into such a scheme, that it can be reasoned about at all. Part of the technique of science is to universalize its subject matter and we know perfectly well how it sets about doing so. In so far as it succeeds, everything in the world is bound to be necessary. But it succeeds only at a sacrifice of the particularity of phenomena and indeed of change and the natural outcome of its efforts is to deny both plurality and change so that the world becomes a universal, or an individual, as one prefers. It follows therefore that in recognizing particularity, the scientist can make no deductions and can discover no necessity. Hence his choice lies—as we indicated in our discussion of *Identité et Réalité*—between denying experience (time and plurality) and retaining reason or denying reason (immutability and unity) and retaining experience. Whereas the one course may satisfy one instinct, the other certainly satisfies another.

To return to our exposition, it is certain that no set of deductions was ever purely rational (*ES* 70). There have been empirical elements in them all. But this simply means that mankind here as so often elsewhere has aimed higher that it can hit. It always hopes moreover to eliminate the empirical elements as soon as it can and to replace them with logical deductions, to substitute *vérités de droit* for *vérités de fait* (*Ib.*). This has been admitted even in biology where deduction is usually less successful than in physics. M. Meyerson cites Cuvier on the interrelation of the various organs to demonstrate the place of reasoning in reconstructing extinct animals which survive only in skeletal fragments.

"Il constate qu'un ' animal qui ne peut digérer que de la chair doit, sous peine de destruction, avoir la faculté d'apercevoir son gibier, de le poursuivre, de le saisir, de le dépecer . . . Ainsi jamais une dent tranchante et propre à découper la chair ne coexistera dans la même espèce avec un pied enveloppé de corne, qui ne peut que soutenir l'animal et avec lequel il ne peut saisir. De là la règle que tout animal à sabot est herbivore; et ces règles encore plus détaillées, qui ne sont que les corollaires de la première, que des sabots aux pieds indiquent des dents molaires à couronne plate, un canal alimentaire très long, un estomac ample ou multiple, et un grand nombre d'autres rapports du même genre.' Ce sont là des lois qui 'ont, pour ainsi dire, été déduites, par le raisonnement, des connaissances que nous avions de l'influence réciproque des fonctions et de l'usage de chaque organe. L'observation les ayant confirmées, nous nous trouvons en droit de suivre une marche contraire dans d'autres circonstances; et lorsque l'observation nous montre des rapports constants de forme entre certains organes, nous devons en conclure qu'ils exercent quelque action l'un sur l'autre.'' (*ES* 71.)

It is worth pointing out, however, that assuming Cuvier's reasoning to be correct, it *becomes* deductive because of the establishment into a general law of an empirical observation. For there is nothing *a priori* impossible in imagining carnivorous animals which only attack a sleeping prey or which, as is true of some insects, paralyse it before eating it or kill it by exuding from a distance a cloud of poisonous gas or hypnotise it (as cobras are said to do in literary romances). Such animals would have no more need of claws than the dog has. Similar reflections could be made upon the animal's alimentary canal. There is no *a priori* reason why a carnivorous animal should not have a short canal if his digestive juices were more plentiful or more potent nor for that matter why it should grind its food by teeth rather than by a rotating grinder nor why it should chew at all instead of dissolving its food. Given, however, animals such as we have, Cuvier's reasoning sounds profound and, to one who is not a biologist at least, almost water-tight. But it derives its plausibility not from its deductive rigor but from its adherence to facts. All that Cuvier has done to his facts is to arrange them in logical order but one could reverse the order and make it equaly logical and equally telling. For instead of starting with the general law that the digestive system determines the outer anatomy, one could maintain that an animal with sharp teeth, speedy legs, clawed feet, etc., is determined to seek prey which runs aways, has to be cut up, etc.[8]

[8] The same thing is true in physical science. No one could deduce from rational grounds alone that a molecule of three atoms of oxygen should have properties which are qualitatively different from those of a molecule of two atoms. At most one would infer that the properties of O_2 were intensified by 1/2 in O_3, which of course is not true. If now we could find some general chemical property peculiar to molecules consisting of three atoms of the same element, then we could infer logically that a supposititious molecule of the sort would have that property. But here—as in our biological example—the deduction is more apparent than real, and though we should argue that X_3 would have these properties, it would follow from the premise—based upon empirical foundations—that "all molecules composed of three atoms of the same element have such and such properties." We see this process at work in the actual deductions made by scientists when

Nevertheless, it is true that a deduction such as Cuvier's does appear more satisfying than a simple note coupling the cause and effect without asserting the logical connection between them. Whence comes that satisfaction? It comes from an absorption of temporal succession into logical succession (*ES* 76). But logical succession, as we shall see, is really a denial of succession, inasmuch as one deduces from premises only what is already in them. Hence deduction becomes an assertion of the essential identity of the terms it utilizes. That is why physical explanation by impact (*ES* 81) seems so much more reasonable than other types, for although impact itself is inexplicable, it alone is successful in preserving the desired eleaticism of reality. That is why also the creation of *êtres fictifs,* such as caloric or phlogiston, does not shock us. They *pass* from one phenomenon to another (*ES* 88) and thus provide a lasting identity.

But deduction could not hold good of reality unless reality were rational. To explain what is meant by the conformity of nature to reason is perhaps best accomplished by indicating faculties of the human mind to which it does not conform. We know for instance that there is no essential harmony between the sequence of events and our desires, nor be-

---

they introduce new assumptions. These assumptions are admittedly made to make the deductions come out right. This is so brilliantly illustrated in Euclidean geometry in the failure to prove the parallel postulate. But it is the parallel postulate which makes Euclidean *geometry* "Euclidean"—that is, agreeable to our spatial intuitions.

tween the sequence of events and our creative imagination. In fact one of the problems of ethics is to make these two faculties—if I may be permitted this antique term—conform to nature. Hence the phrase is meaningful, though exactly what its meaning is may as yet be none too precise. At any rate, one finds the conformity of nature and reason asserted by the early Greeks. Anaxagoras and before him Hermotimas, said Aristotle (*ES* 97), explained this by maintaining that nature was the seat of a governing principle, or intelligence. Whether we choose this explanation or not, the assertion of this conformity is essential to science (*ES* 98). Even positivistic science requires interpolations and extrapolations and these are performed by reason and in accordance with rational rules.[9]

Yet it should be noticed that this presupposition has forced the scientist of to-day, as it forced the Greeks, to deny the reality of plurality and change. Neither of these aspects of nature are rational and only Heraclitans—though not Heraclitus himself—seem to have admitted that they were as "legitimate" a property of the natural order as unity and immutability. But the Heraclitans in admitting this willingly concluded that therefore nature was not

[9] Recently, see above, more emphasis has been put upon the difficulty of extrapolating without a fairly constant experimental verification. We find that we cannot always extrapolate into the "microscopic world." Nevertheless this appears anomalous to us and there is no doubt that physicists would feel easier if the discontinuity could be explained away.

rational and that therefore discourse was vain and the logical outcome seemed to them to be the nihilism of the sophist Gorgias.[10] Therefore the presupposition of nature's rationality implied the " unnaturalness " of human experience, so that either a new technique of interpreting reality was needed or a great slice of nature was left beyond the reach of science.

This conformity of nature and reason is to-day best illustrated in the conviction that nature " jusqu'au plus profond de ses manifestations, est gouvernée inéluctablement par des lois rigoureuses " (*ES* 99). This opinion does not seem to have been shared by Comte who believed that our laws would not always prove compatible with too detailed an investigation of nature. He did not mean that our laws require revision as our knowledge increases, but that beneath the orderly plane of nature is a plane which is submitted to no law at all, " un amas de faits confus, entièrement soustraits à toute règle, en tant du moins qu'il s'agit de règles connaissables de nous " (*ES* 101). If this is Comte's meaning, then he anticipated one of the most " modern " of modern scientific theories. No one would maintain that the microscopic world was a collection of beings *entièrement soustraits à toute règle,* yet many physicists would maintain that the rules governing it hold only for the mass and that there is a principle of inde-

[10] These remarks must of course be taken with a grain of salt, since what we know of these thinkers is very little and very unreliable.

terminacy at the very heart of nature.[11] The generality and uniformity of these laws—and probably of all laws—is not a property of nature but a property of our formulæ; nature approximates them but does not reach them. Hence the conformity of nature to reason cannot even be assumed to be complete.

M. Meyerson points out that the objective existence of chance was not unsuspected in antiquity (*ES* 101). Both Plato and Aristotle, in spite of their pronounced rationalism, admitted the existence of fortuitous events but maintained that they could find no place in science and the very existence of hazard, even outside the realm of science, was denied by the Stoics whose philosophy dominated the post-classical world. As for modern indeterminism, of which we have been speaking, M. Meyerson does not believe that it confirms the views of Comte (*ES* 102). Writing before the elaboration of the modern quantum theory, he maintains that we use the laws of probability in the microscopic world " parce que nous ignorons l'enchaînement véritable des phénomènes moléculaires, atomiques, sous-atomiques, etc., et que ce procédé nous permet précisément de faire abstraction de cette ignorance, d'éliminer (pour nous servir

[11] I am thinking of course of the Heisenberg principle. Its meaning philosophically is not perhaps quite clear. It states the impossibility of having the two sets of data necessary for determining a future state. Some philosophers might object that this implied an indeterminancy of prediction but not of event. To make this distinction eliminates the " operational " theory of meaning and the basis of the theory of relativity—at least of the special theory. But see A. O. Lovejoy: *The Revolt Against Dualism,* N. Y., 1930, p. 286 ff.

d'une image mathématique) cette inconnue de nos calculs, en ne commettant que des erreurs qui, tant qu'il s'agit de phénomènes molaires, phénomènes grossiers par conséquent, restent imperceptibles. Mais nous n'en demeurons pas moins convaincus que les phénomènes sous-jacents, moléculaires, etc., obéissent eux aussi à une légalité tout à fait stricte" (*ES* 103). We have already discussed this point of view above and we see no reason for changing our opinion. For even in the macroscopic world our measurements are averages, our generalizations are statistical, whereas our explanations are based on *êtres fictifs*. A probability does not change its nature because its fraction approaches unity; it is always a probability. As for ignorance, it should be noted that complete ignorance would give us no data whatsoever and without data we could no more calculate a probability than construct a causal explanation. As a matter of fact our ignorance in the microscopic world is the same in kind as in the macroscopic; it is admittedly an ignorance of *causation*. The causation in the macroscopic world is constructed *ad hoc;* if the world were so and so then the observed experiments would follow. We know, however, from elementary logic how shaky such reasoning is. We also know how short has been the lives of such explanations; they die as soon as an experiment can be performed which they cannot explain. If now we have not been able to construct an explanation of microscopic events, it may be that we are looking for something that does not exist. At any rate it will be admitted that in this realm our ignorance—if one wishes to speak of that—has increased rather than diminished and that the use of statistics has been more and more accepted as the legitimate way of interpreting these phenomena.

There is no doubt that as far as the group is concerned the regularity of statistical law approaches that of causal law. But what that shows is that under certain conditions, certain events will tend to occur and in no way gives any ground for suspecting the endurance of an underlying identity. Hence the ability to formulate statistical generalizations may give one the right to assert a strict determinism, as seems to be suggested in a passage quoted by M. Meyerson from Sophie Germain (*ES* 103). But there is a sense in which determinism may be asserted without the implication of Meyersonian causality, i. e., identity. One has only to consider the case we have mentioned before, the vector law of the parallelogram of forces. No one would deny that this law held good within the limits of measurement, nor that the vector was strictly determined by the two directions which form the two adjacent sides of the parallelogram. But by no stretch of the imagination can the vector be said to be either " in " the sides separately or in their combination, unless one wishes to introduce the notion of " potentiality " which would certainly obscure rather than clarify the issue. Hence even if statistical laws do imply determinism for the group, they imply nothing whatsoever for the individual; and even if they lead one to think that the general trend of the particular events in question is such and such, and cannot occur without the previous occurrence of certain determinants, they give no evidence whatsoever of an identity between these determinants and what they determine. Thus whatever Comte's own opinion may have been about the laws governing the microscopic world, it is clear that one may have statistical generalizations and determinism without causality as defined in M. Meyerson's works.

But no matter how binding the determinism seems, sooner or later one has to reach the point where it is a matter of chance whether *A* or not-*A* occurs. Suppose we were able to trace the movement of the molecules (or groups of molecules) in a drop of oil or in a gas from moment to moment, we should either have to go back to infinity—which is obviously no explanation and is moreover impossible—or we should have to stop at a given point. If this point was arbitrarily chosen, we should have tacitly accepted what we set out to explain. If it was actually the beginning of the movement, it is obviously impossible to explain why this direction and this velocity should be exhibited by the various molecules rather than any other, since any change in velocity or direction can only be explained by the collision with other velocities and directions and these by hypothesis did not exist. If now the velocities and directions are not determined atomistically but organistically—i. e., whenever the molecules are in a given spatial relation they will begin to move in such directions and with such velocities, reciprocally determined—then again it can only be a matter of chance whether they are or are not in such an arrangement. A matter of chance, because there is no way of telling why they should be in that arrangement rather than in any other. And there is no way, not because we happen to be ignorant of how that arrangement was produced, but simply because the very terms of our theory prevent any explanation, no matter how much we know. For we can either suppose the right arrangement to have lasted from eternity or from a finite time and we are in a situation exactly analogous to that in which velocities and directions are explained atomistically. My expression of these two theories is of course both too simple and too narrow—there may be other forms of theory. But the same reasoning can be applied to any theory which explains posterior events by anterior. Whether the initial state is called an irrational or a chance event is of no moment.

In spite of these considerations, the very existence of law—regardless of cause—implies a conformity between nature and reason. If there were none, action based upon foresight would be impossible and the simplest predictions would be futile (*ES* 112). But this implies an ontology which would permit laws to hold good of the world, which would provide for the repetition of events. This ontology is tacitly assumed by the scientist whenever he sets to work. Duhem has shown how in the past scientific theories were prolongations of metaphysics—*vide* those of the Peripatetics, the Atomists, the Cartesians (*ES* 114). We might add the evidence which Mr. Burtt has recently adduced in his *Metaphysical Foundations of Modern Science.* In recent times this method of attack has become rarer, perhaps because of the influence of positivism (*ES* 115) [12] but more likely because of the electrical theory of matter. But even here the physicist reasons about atoms, electrons and protons, as if they were real things and not concepts. How else could we reason when we strive to differentiate the true from the false laws of nature? Such a differentiation necessitates some consideration of the nature of things (*ES* 116). Mechanics and electro-dynamics consist of laws which are supposed to hold good of certain entities supposed to be ultimate, " comme constituant la trame réelle des choses et comme devant, par conséquent, servir à expliquer tous les autres phénomènes " (*ES* 117). Whether the laws of mechanics or of electro-dynamics are held to be true of the ultimate nature of the universe is not determined by a superi-

[12] This is a very interesting admission on M. Meyerson's part, that sciences is changing. For when used in connection with his main thesis, as expressed in *Identité et Réalité,* it implies that perhaps the a *priori* elements of thought are changing. Might not this be an evolution analogous to that of logicality out of pre-logicality, as suggested by the studies of M. Lévy-Bruhl?

ority of the laws themselves but of a theory as to whether *la trame réelle des choses* is mechanical or electrical (*ES* 118). An example is easily afforded in the field of astrophysics. It is clear that we cannot formulate laws of the behaviour of the planets, until we have first formulated some idea of what this behaviour " really " is. The scientist may not believe that he yet knows what the nature of things " really " is and indeed he attributes the imperfection of his laws to the circumstance of his relative ignorance. And he feels that he cannot complete his scientific knowledge until he has gained a further penetration into the nature of reality.[13] Such penetration in turn is rendered possible by one thing, the rationality of nature. This will appear not only in causalism but also in positivism, for if the former believes that the accord between nature and reason is lodged in the existence of causal entities, the latter believes it is lodged in the existence of order at least as described in its laws. Science therefore, even positivistic science, is bound to be realistic (*ES* 121).

But the rationality of nature is also attested outside of science, by the fact that man has always reasoned about nature. If he has reasoned, he has

[13] This obviously re-introduces the question of what the nature of anything is aside from its behaviour. In this instance, M. Meyerson cites the incapacity of the Ptolemaic theory to explain the movements of the planets as evidence that it did not understand the real nature of those movements, i. e., their heliocentricity. But why is heliocentricity any more the nature and less the behaviour of planetary motion than geocentricity?

necessarily believed nature to be rational, and if rational, *deducible.* It is thus that he identifies "cause" and "sufficient reason."[14] Upon that faith in the rationality of nature he has built his hope of a complete deduction of all events (*la déduction totale de la nature*). No one, says M. Meyerson (*ES* 121), has expressed this better than the Stoics to whom the complete causal linkage of events was based upon the complete unity of nature. Whence not only were all phenomena determined, but their linkage was necessary.

From this source we can derive the cause of the similarity between temporal and logical succession. Though in our scientific explorations we usually move from effect to cause (looking for the explanation of the phenomenon), when we reason about them we go from cause to effect. The explanation of this anomaly is that in our minds the causal and the logical series are one (*ES* 125). It is thus that as the logically posterior is implicit in the logically anterior, so the causally posterior must be implicit in the causally anterior.[15]

[14] In Leibnitz, however, the two are separated and the sufficient reason is at least in places interpreted teleologically. See, e. g., *Monadology,* 53, 54.

[15] Although this may be the reason, there is another possibility, namely, that "*p* implies *q* does not imply that *q* implies *p*." One can reason from antecedent to consequent but not from consequent to antecedent unless one has the additional premise that the given antecedent is the only antecedent. But how could that premise be acquired? This holds good for logical deductions and for scientific explanations. Just as there is an indefinite number of possible premises for any conclusion, so there is an indefinite number of possible causes

It is the identity between the two which permits deductions to hold good of nature and it is the implicitness of the consequent in the antecedent which makes possible the deductive process itself.

M. Meyerson then proceeds to demonstrate how all reasoning is a series of identities substituted one for the other, made possible by preliminary identifications. That reasoning is identification has its historical genesis—as far as we have records—in the Eleatics but has been more definitely articulated in Leibnitz and Condillac in our own times (*ES* 137). This is held to be especially clear in the case of mathematical reasoning which consists in a series of equations, permitting us to omit the intermediate identifications and to skip from the first to the last. Nevertheless mathematical equations are not pure tautologies; they are never purely analytic judgments (*ES* 139). When one says, for instance, $(a + b)(a - b) = a^2 - b^2$, the equality is a discovery and reveals something hitherto unknown to the mathematician. " C'est, sans doute, ce que l'on appelle une equation *identique,* mais l'identité ne saute pas immédiatement aux yeux (du moins pour un débutant en mathématiques), car ce qui se trouve écrit des deux côtés du signe d'égalité n'est pas identique par le fait: c'est d'une part un produit et d'autre part une somme. Le signe d'égalité signifie simplement

(unless one has previous knowledge to the contrary) for any effect. Therefore if the reasoner wishes to avoid a fallacy, he has to move from antecedent to consequent in both cases.

que les choses sont égales par certains côtés ou le seront sous certaines conventions " (*ES* 139). Thus even in mathematics, the equation asserts an identity where there is apparent difference; the beginner in mathematics is surprised that the identity should exist (*ES* 143). In other words in reasoning thought does not formulate an identity already existing in our minds but introduces an identity where it was unsuspected (*ES* 145.)

This process M. Meyerson calls " identification " and insists that it is *un point tout à fait fondamental de la théorie du raisonnement* (*Ib.*). He illustrates this by a beautiful and now famous passage on the proof of the Pythagorean theorem. Nevertheless one must feel a certain hesitancy in view of bits of reasoning which do not—at least at first sight—appear to include identifications or even equations. I have found no discussion of such reasoning in our author and hence introduce it here. One of the simplest examples is the following:

$$a > b,$$
$$b > c,$$
$$a > c.$$

Here even a verbal expression with " is " in it does not mislead us into seeing an identification in it. If we write

$$a = \text{an-entity-greater-than-}b,$$
$$b = \text{an-entity-greater-than-}c,$$
$$a = \text{an-entity-greater-than-}c,$$

one might even be tempted to conclude that $a = b$,

if reasoning by identification is involved [16] and if "an-entity-greater-than-c" means exactly the same thing in both equations, which of course it does not. But that it does not would never appear from the equations.

One may again symbolize this reasoning as follows:

$a = b + M$ (where M is a positive whole number),
$b = c + N$ (where N is a positive whole number),
$a = c + N + M$,
$a > c$.

But even this does not rid the demonstration of the relation $>$, since the reasoning contains a concealed premise, "A number is greater than any of the numbers whose sum it equals."

The basis of this reasoning is what we know of the relation, *greater-than,* namely, that it is transitive and asymmetrical. If we know that any relation is transitive and asymmetrical, we can reason by its aid. But the same thing is true of other types of relation, of which $=$ is only one. Is it not therefore probable that reasoning by identification is more usual but no more fundamental than reasoning by any other relation and that its justification is in its relational properties? If so, the rationality of the world cannot be its capacity for identity but on the contrary its relatedness. And, to repeat, all forms

[16] It is obvious that $=$ is used for the copula "is" and is hence misleading.

of relations do not lend themselves to the identification of their relata but on the contrary some presuppose their fundamental difference.

M. Meyerson, however, does not appear to recognize these other types of relational reasoning and consequently for him the problem next becomes one of discovering the identity which is supposed to justify the identification. In the demonstration of the Pythagorean theorem referred to above, certain rectangles and squares are said to be equal which have every appearance of inequality; their identity lies in their area (*ES* 148). But the area of the two figures is a quantitative property which is a function of two variables appearing both in the square and the rectangle. It is that quantitative property—the product of two adjacent sides—which we discover to be the same in each figure. This is typical, it is maintained (*ES* 149), of all mathematical deduction; it presents us with a *cascade d'équations* which exhibits identities by considering the terms from a single determined point of view.

It is that conclusion which prevents M. Meyerson from accepting Jevon's account of reasoning as a "substitution of similars." The substitution of similars would make reasoning a series of tautologies, whereas it is really a process of identifications. Identification is not only the act by which we recognize the identical where it exists, but also the act by which we reduce to identity that which first seemed non-identical (*ES* 154). But the process of identification itself depends upon our power of generalization—by which we see in a group of objects their common properties. This power permits us to discuss " any " triangle, or " the " triangle, just as in chemistry it permits us to discuss " sulfur " or " silver " without regard to the peculiarities of the individual specimens we have at hand (*ES* 155). Thus we confine our remarks to the similarities and neglect the dissimilarities, and out of them construct the subject matter of science.

In mathematics the identities are not built up in this way. The equality which the mathematician perceives between the area of a square and a rectangle is something established by reasoning. " C'est l'énoncé du théorème, et le fait que cet énoncé est suivi d'une démonstration prouve précisément qu'il n'y a là rien que l'on puisse percevoir immédiatement, mais quelque chose qu'il faut établir, qu'il faut rechercher des similitudes, des identités, afin de parvenir, par leur enchaînement, à celle que l'on vise (*ES* 156)." It is therefore not immediately perceived but deduced.[17] That is why there is a certain resistance to mathematical demonstration.

[17] It is a grave question in the writer's mind whether anything which can be symbolized by a proposition can be immediately perceived. All immediate judgments which he is familiar with have behind them a history of experimentation (manipulation) which seems to be in the nature of satisfying curiosity, after which they *become* immediate. Observation of children will probably show that what seem like ultra-rapid perceptions in adults—the identification of colors, sounds, etc.,—are surprisingly slow in infants, though he has no experimental evidence of any scientific value to advance in

From the process of identification arises the principle of equality between cause and effect. Otherwise causality would furnish no grounds whatsoever for rational deduction. This has been most clearly perceived by Leibnitz who declared that " l'effet intégral peut reproduire la cause entière ou son semblable " and that " l'effet entier est toujours équivalent à sa cause pleine." This seemed so obvious to him that he used it in a *reductio ad absurdum.* " Il s'ensuivrait que la cause ne pourrait être restituée en entier, ni substituée à son effet, ce qui, on le comprend aisément, est entièrement contraire aux habitudes de la nature et aux raisons des choses," he says in trying to prove that a proposition is false (*ES* 157).

The question now arises of why the underlying identity of things should be obscured. Cause and effect are identical, although time has elapsed between them. Things seem to have changed although we believe the change to be superficial. What then diversifies things? In answer to this question M. Meyerson points out that things as a whole are submitted to only two general conditions, time and space. The causal postulate tends to eliminate time, leaving space. Thus the only thing left to be modi-

support of this thesis. In mathematics the "identities" are more difficult to perceive, no doubt, but when one is skilled in mathematics as one is in simple sensory experiments, they become remarkably rapid. It should never be forgotten that the "natural history" of a stimulus-response tends to telescope—as is seen in the learning process—and that there is therefore no particular reason to accept the already telescoped experiences as a special genus.

fied is the spatial arrangement of things and the most perfect explanation will consist in showing that what would have existed before will exist afterwards, that nothing has been created and that nothing has been lost, that no change has occurred *except in spatial arrangement.* " L'explication la plus parfaite d'un changement ne peut consister qu'en sa réduction à une fonction spatiale " (*ES* 159).

The examples of this in science are plentiful. Many are given in *Identité et Réalité.* They run back to Democritus and Lucretius and continue to the present day—see the discussions of the Solway Congress already referred to. They appear in the various principles of conservation. They are seen even in non-quantitative theories, such as the peripatetic doctrine of substantial forms—we might add the contemporary Anglo-American epistemological doctrines of " neutral entities " and " essences." Even when we cannot clearly imagine what exactly persists in time—and we cannot when we write chemical equations—the satisfaction we derive from such persistence overbalances our resistance. The need of a persistent entity is greater than the need of a clear image. This is so true that even when we have an entity which is a scientific abstraction, we tend to hypostatise it into a thing (*ES* 162).[18]

Omitting the expression of identification in biology (in the theory of preformationism), we can immedi-

[18] See especially the paragraph beginning "Ce n'est pas là, pour nous, une constatation nouvelle . . ."

ately jump to M. Meyerson's conclusion which treats the question of explaining the eternal as well as the changing. He cites Aristotle's criticism of Democritus, to the effect that one cannot satisfy the reason by maintaining that an event is properly explained by saying that it has existed forever (*ES* 179). On the contrary, one must also explain the cause of that eternal persistence. As Leibnitz said, if the world has always existed and is made up of globules, one must explain why globules instead of cubes (*ES* 180). For God would not have given the ultimate particles of matter one form instead of another arbitrarily. This is admittedly a widening of the concept of causality and yet there is an intimate connection between the two (*ES* 182). In the explanation of change, our problem is to reduce it to a persistent identity; in the explanation of the eternal, our problem is to explain diversity. In both cases we deny the existence of that which we set out to prove (*ES* 183). This gives us the concept of homogeneous matter whose properties other than spatial are bound to seem "occult." But when we have identified this matter with space, then its properties become rational and we can have a deductive theory of matter.[19]

That the history of science proves this, we may in accordance with our practice accept as true. Yet that science has asked an intelligible question seems

[19] But why the question does not arise of why space is of one type rather than another is left untouched by M. Meyerson.

doubtful to us. M. Meyerson refers to an opinion of Saint Thomas's to the effect that *natures* are inexplicable—*il n'y a pas de raison des natures.* We cannot but feel that on this point Saint Thomas speaks more wisely than Leibnitz. For the question of why God made globules rather than cubes can only arise if one presupposes that there was a time when there were neither globules nor cubes—which is contrary to the terms of our discussion.[20] If one has a genuinely eternal or absolutely general event, one has to have recourse to a "nature." Thus one can explain why a moving body changes its direction, but cannot in the long run explain why it continues its direction. Similarly one cannot seek to explain why Newtonian gravitation should vary directly as the product of the masses and inversely as the square of the distance, rather than as the difference between the masses and the cube of the distance, but one could seek to explain a variation from the law. In fact the very formula of the principle of sufficient reason as given by Leibnitz (*ES* 181 and n. 1) shows that a reason *for this rather than that* is sought—*cur sit potius quam non sit aut cur sit potius quam aliter.* But if something is really eternal or absolutely general, the questions *cur non sit* and *cur non sit aliter* do not arise. If this were not so, the number of questions that might arise would be endless. For the ways in which a thing might be otherwise

[20] Add to this the fact that Leibnitz admits God's reasons to be often inaccessible to man.

than it is, are practically infinite in number. The value of scientific generalizations, we should maintain, is precisely to delimit the ways in which things are, so that grotesque questions do not arise. One may ask legitimately why things apparently fall with varying velocities, but if they fell with uniform velocity, it would be absurd to ask why. One might as well ask why a certain number of ether vibrations per second (or whatever they turn out to be) should be red and another number green.

III

The acceptance of certain facts as facts is inevitable (cf. *ES* 214), just as the use of indefinables in a deductive system is inevitable. Yet the acceptance of certain facts means the rejection of explaining them, since they are that which explains all else in the universe of discourse.

Besides these basic facts there are certain other inexplicable elements in any rational science which, as we have seen in our discussion of *Identité et Réalité,* are called *irrationals.* At the very outset of thought appears a concept which resists every attempt to make it rational, to wit, the "many." Science cannot contemplate diversity without trying to reduce it to unity and yet without diversity the reason could not operate at all. As soon as thinking appears, it takes as its problem the simplification of appearance. In the special sciences one sees similar irrationals. In geometry appears the spatial quality of tri-dimensionality which philosophers have sometimes tried to deduce but which we now know is inherent in the parallel postulate (*ES* 188).[21] That space has this quality rather than some other has to be accepted as a fact, regardless of whether geometry be a science based upon intuitions or not. One might, without contradicting anything M. Meyerson says, extend this observation and conclude that *specificity* is always bound to be inexplicable, being strictly analogous to what he calls (*ES* 189) the physical irrational, sensory qualities. For what is inexplicable in physics is, e. g., how a given sound is produced by a given air wave or, if one prefer, why a series of homogeneous motions should give rise to a collection of heterogeneous qualities. That the collection exists cannot, I suppose, be questioned. So in any universe of discourse the specificity of the subject matter has to be accepted just as its plurality has to be accepted. Yet there is a tendency to disregard it as there is to disregard multiplicity, witness the attempts to prove that geometry is " nothing but " algebra, chemistry " nothing but " physics, biology " nothing but " mechanics, psychology " nothing but " physiology, and the like. All that " nothing but " can mean in practice is that the problems in question can be correlated with certain causes which have not their specific character. But even if this were possible—and no one has as yet

[21] Each kind of non-Euclidean geometry would be subject of course to analogous remarks.

completely done it in any large field—it would not imply that a laryngeal twitching was a thought or a living wage a sentiment of patriotism. And the problem would still remain how something which was nothing but something else could sometimes seem so different.

The physical irrationals, sensory qualities and transitive action, we have already discussed. The first is inevitably made inexplicable as soon as the true essence of things is said to be matter and motion, for who could deduce *a priori* a color from a given wave length? Similarly transitive action can never be explained. No one knows what happens when two masses collide and a whole group of philosophers has shown why.[22] But is the irrationality of sensation any different in kind from any other case of causation? There is no way *a priori* of knowing what effect will follow from any cause; experience alone can tell. After our observation is generalized, it is a simple matter to predict the effect from the cause or even to invent an explanation—by the principle of persisting identity—of the causality. But what we are empirically given is that natural history whose *terminus ad quem* is the effect and whose *terminus a quo* the cause, and we can chop it up into as finely divided parts as we desire. The interaction of human and non-human nature is not

22 And, as M. Meyerson says (*ES* 199), science has given up the attempt to find out without even reading what the philosophers have said on the subject.

ostensibly different, as far as the production of sensation is concerned. As for transitive action, it might be concluded that we are looking for something which is not there. That was the conclusion of the positivists, and legality was substituted for causality. This does not prevent our discussing the only kind of causation which is observable, namely the interaction of different natural histories or events, but it must deprive us of all right to assert persisting identities underlying them. Yet it is the principle of identity which alone makes transitive action seem reasonable and any move to give it up gives up any hope of *explaining* mechanical causation. What can take its place? As far as the present writer sees, only legality, which after all is merely positivistic description—whether phenomenalistic or not we shall not discuss.

But this is not all. The trend of science has been to reduce matter to space (or space-time) and in this *arché* is no condition of diversity.[23] Newton lays it down—probably as a reflection on Descartes (*ES* 201 n. 1)—that *a caeca necessitate metaphysica quae utique eadem est semper et ubique, nulla oritur rerum variatio.* This is shown by M. Meyerson to be a continuation of the Parmenidean tradition according to which the *particular* cannot be deduced. The same reasoning holds good for temporal particularity. Yet change is what science feeds upon and if it were entirely irrational, no scientific laws

[23] Modern space-time, however, is in itself heterogeneous.

would be deducible at all. Science has tried to render change rational by treating it as a spatial rearrangement of permanent elements. But this treatment can never be complete. The second law of thermodynamics shows why real mechanical change can never be reversible and without reversibility no identity can be established between antecedent and consequent and hence no rational explanation is possible (*ES* 204).[24] We have already seen how little "plausible" is the Carnot-Clausius principle and what attempts have been made to deny or explain away its finality. By means of statistics the increase of entropy is seen to be a movement towards a more probable distribution of elements and thus the second law is rationalized. Nevertheless this is at the expense of another irrational, namely the initial improbable distribution of the elements from which we can escape only by supposing it the consequent of a prior more probable state (*ES* 215). But this involves us in a postulate of cycles which M. Meyerson has shown to be objectionable (*ES* 211).

These irrationals and others (*ES* 216 ff.) are inevitable. Every science will have some of its own and no matter how far deduction will push its domain, there will always remain unconquered territory. (Indeed the fact that a science has any spe-

[24] It will be recalled that for M. Meyerson deduction is (as for Poincaré) a "cascade of equations." Yet it is interesting that the very mathematical deduction of the second law results in an inequality and that from that inequality a host of inferences are drawn.

cific subject matter shows that there will always be irrationals.) If all natural events were deducible, there would be no need of experimentation and, if we accept the principle that the progress of science denotes the basic laws of human thinking, we must not discount the importance of the growth rather than the decline of the empirical method.

An experiment can corroborate but cannot prove a proposition, unless the proposition is known to be the only one possible—in which case experimentation is unnecessary. It can disprove a proposition and thus eliminate the number of possibilities to be considered. But it is after all an individual event and in isolation might be thought to warrant only a particular proposition. Yet, as everyone knows, the classical logic does not permit reasoning without universal propositions and the problem of the empiricist is to justify his generalizations. It is obvious that if the universal propositions of Aristotelian logic are to be taken seriously, experimentation would be of very limited use in founding them. Fortunately the scientist does not take them seriously and for him " all " means " on the whole." He is not therefore surprised by the appearance of exceptions but he hopes to calculate their probability. Consequently when he reasons about the universe, he knows that there is bound to be a margin more or less extensive between his conclusions and empirically observed reality, just as he expects such a margin between mathematical and physical entities.

But if the world is not completely deducible, deduction cannot be a cascade of equations. It is our opinion that identification—the meaning of this term has been explained above—is indeed a form of deduction but not the only form. Whenever there is a relation between A and B and we know the nature of the relation, i. e., whether it is symmetrical, transitive, etc., or not, we can reason. The presence of a term is irrelevant to reasoning. Its properties insofar as they are not relative are logically sterile. That is why it can be replaced by x and y in propositional functions. The point is emphasized to show why identification is not universally required. I do not mean to suggest that in other forms of reasoning every detail in the world is deducible; on the contrary, there will always be irrationals no matter what form of reasoning is used.

But if reasoning has as its aim the explanation of the world, it is clear that it must be judged by its fruits. Now reasoning as presented by M. Meyerson is in a singularly paradoxical condition. It requires multiplicity and specificity as its subject matter and yet it denies them reality. It interprets reality in terms of causality and finds itself unable to give an intelligible account of causality. It corrects its deductions by means of observation, yet insists that observation is a film of appearance over the substratum of rationality. Would it not seem to follow that its method was in serious need of correction and that if its results are trustworthy, their trustworthiness were accidental?

Sooner or later the concepts of science can trace their ancestry back to the plebeian notions of common sense. The concept of causation is one whose lineage is among the least dubious. Whereas one cannot argue that the common-sense meaning of a term is the correct meaning—since all meanings are arbitrary—nevertheless it may clarify to a certain extent the connotation of the term in question. Now it is certain that in common-sense some situations are said to be causal in which the effect is *in* the cause (thus establishing identity) only metaphorically. When we say that a certain poison causes death, we certainly do not mean that there is an identity between the poison and death, nor that any of the properties of a dead body are shared by the poison. We mean, on the contrary, that the poison + the body = a dead body and that presumably as much has happened to the poison as to the body. One could, I presume, work up a theory according to which death was *in* the poison or the poison was potentially a dead body, but it does not seem a likely candidate for wide acceptance. In physical science we have an exact counterpart in the law of the parallelogram of forces, an example which we have already used, or indeed in any case where the result is the product of two (or more) antecedent causes. A product is in neither its multiplier nor in its mutiplicand; it does not exist until the multiplication is completed. Obviously we can write it in the form of an equation —$a \,.\, b = ab$. But—as M. Meyerson himself has pointed out in an analogous situation—that is, if not a tautology, the expression of an operation: it is the multiplication-symbol here which is important. For a and b can be combined in ways which are not equal to ab.[25] This is of course only a symbol but it indicates a number of situations in which the effect is much more than its causes taken as so much stuff: it is its causes in such and such a combination, nor can they be recovered until another operation has been performed. Any vector laws will illustrate this.[26]

M. Meyerson's comment on these remarks would probably be that they confuse legality with causality. But our question concerns the possibility of discovering the causality which underlies the events so formulated. We are not blind to the fact that one can devise metaphors according to which the effect will be "potentially" *in* the cause or causes, but these metaphors will provide no enlightenment whatsoever as to what takes place. There will always be an *operation*—if only transitive action—which will escape analysis and as long as that is true, the scientist is a positivist whether he knows it or not and not a "causalist." There is therefore nothing gained by calling transitive action an irrational. It is a

[25] It is obvious and unnecessary to remark that in this example a can be added to itself b times and the result will be ab. But this does not obviate the difficulty that an operation is indicated on the left hand of the equation. I mention this simply because I have met it as an objection in conversation.

[26] Cf. G. R. Montgomery, "The Meaning of Analysis," *J. of Philos.* I, 651.

peculiar relation between terms whose characteristics can be determined only by observation. But once they are established, they are the facts by means of which reasoning is made possible. For from *a* there is no other passage to *b*. They are therefore the very stuff of reason. If now one has a conception of reason which makes the use of relations—other than that of identity—paradoxical, one's duty is to change it, unless to be sure one's definition is admittedly purely verbal.

That science must admit the existence of specificity and multiplicity while denying their reality is again a reason for insisting that either it is very naive or that it does not take its metaphors seriously. It is true that the Aristotelian concept has no place in the physical world and that if we admit reality to consist of Platonic ideas imperfectly incorporated in Nature, the Newtonian formula cited above, that plurality and change cannot be deduced from unity and permanence, is a necessary conclusion. The correction of deduction by experience is bound to be an anomaly so long as that metaphysics is adhered to. But nothing prevents our turning the tables, admitting the reality of multiplicity and change and denying the reality of unity and permanence, except insofar as it is found. The eleatic qualities admit of no degrees; things cannot be more or less one, more or less permanent. But they do admit of more or less multiplicity and more or less mutability. Unity and permanence as the limits of plurality and change are perfectly intelligible notions. What is more, that interpretation of their being conforms with the statistical method which is more and more typical of science. The scientist may say that ideally the variation in a class ought to be zero, but he has never found such a class nor is there much hope that he ever will. We may not choose to call statistical operations " reasoning " yet that they render natural events intelligible is indubitable. But they do so not by assuming an underlying unity and permanence, but by measuring the variety and impermanence. It is true that a statistical science gives one no absolute certainty, for there is always a finite margin between the fraction of probability and 1. Yet the certainty, which for want of a better name what we shall call "Aristotelian logic " gave one, had the grotesque property of being only rarely true.

We have already tried to arouse the suspicion that the irrationality of sensory qualities (thinking of them as the products of physical motion) is no different in kind from the irrationality of any effect. But it should be further remarked that this again is anomalous only if reason is identification. Certainly if the conclusion of a deduction must be *in* the premises and the effect *in* the cause, there will be no possibility of discovering a sensation in the impact of two bits of matter. But here again the path is open to one to avoid the absurdity by avoiding the premise which gave rise to it. The paradox may be evidence that its premise is false. If the equating of reason and identification produces the paradox that sensation (and by extension other effects) are irrational, one can always deny the equating of reason and identification. Since we have seen that mathematics uses inequalities and natural science other forms of asymmetrical relations, we are under no obligation to deny them this right. But once the right is granted, the paradox vanishes.

The irrationals therefore seem to be a problem only if a peculiar theory of reasoning is advanced. But if they remain irrational, how has one escaped from the most orthodox form of positivism? Causality is bound to be founded upon *êtres fictifs* and the very causal relation appears to be inexplicable, just as Comte and Mach maintained by implication. One cannot deny that science has been causalistic; M. Meyerson's erudition has established that beyond a doubt. But positivism has never denied that as a fact of history. It has been rather a program of reform than a description of the past and one cannot but feel that M. Meyerson's analysis of its method justifies rather than weakens the program.

PART THREE

La Deduction Relativiste

In *Identité et Réalité* we have an attempted demonstration that science has never been positivistic. On the contrary, it seems to have sought two things, (1) constancy and uniformity, an index of an identity underlying phenomena, and (2) a picture of the universe—or at least a part of it—which should start with phenomena but end by explaining away those very characteristics of variability and peculiarity which have in part given rise to their name. This picture would be of the universe as the phenomenon of an over-individual mind—if one chooses to use such language—or better of the universe as it is for any observer, which means for no observer in particular. The question naturally arises why science should seek such a view of the world, why it is not content with the shifting, changing appearances which common sense deals with in practical life. M. Meyerson's answer is the answer of Aristotle and the whole Socratic tradition (and presumably of Parmenides and Heraclitus) that the reason cannot grasp changing things; it deals with being, not with becoming, with universals, not with particulars, with essences, not with existences.

We have already suggested that this difficulty is largely theoretical. The classical logic is based upon the *concept,* which is identical with an essence, permanent and unified but incorporated in the multiple and changing. The relations of the essence to the existent are notoriously mysterious and every reader of the history of philosophy knows what difficulties they produce. We have tried to indicate a kind of reasoning in which the purely symbolic and practical character of the concept is obvious and in which relations of all kinds take the place of essential equalities.[1] But there is no need to develop this idea here.

Having made out a case which, to say the least, is extremely impressive, as far as science up to the twentieth century is concerned, M. Meyerson was confronted with the Einstein theory. At first sight it would certainly appear as if relativistic physics were in direct violation of what M. Meyerson had found in earlier scientific theories. Seventeenth and eighteenth century physics had been willing to adopt a kind of restricted relativity, the relativity of position and velocity at least, but in Einstein and his successors the very mass of objects had melted into a function of their velocities and their velocities were measured in times which were presumably as individual as the systems of reference with respect to which they were measured. Moreover the nature of things, insofar as it was of interest to physics, seemed to be a function of our capacity of measur-

[1] This is unavoidably ambiguous or worse in English. I do not mean "essential equalities" as opposed to "accidental equalities," but "essence-equalities" or "the equating of essences."

ing it and our capacity was obviously in part a function of our peculiar psychophysical constitution. Thus in discussing the famous definition of the basic concept " simultaneity," Einstein said, " We require a definition of simultaneity such that this definition supplies us with the method by means of which . . . [the physicist] can decide by experiment whether or not both [of two events] occurred simultaneously. As long as this requirement is not satisfied, I allow myself to be deceived as a physicist . . . when I imagine that I am able to attach a meaning to the statement of simultaneity."[2]

It will be noted that the meaning of a scientific concept is a function of our ability to detect its meaning experimentally, which here means " perceptually." This surely looks like positivism, for all that can be actually detected is something perceptual and it is obvious that the experimental *mise-en-scène* was designed to afford a phenomenalistic test of a physical concept. " Simultaneity at a distance," as everyone knows, means for Einstein the occurrence of two events such that an observer stationed midway between them will observe light signals emanating from them in one specious present at the observer's location.

The use of " operational " definitions is general in the new physics.[3] So long as it is adhered to, sci-

[2] *Relativity,* N. Y. (Holt), 1920, p. 26.

[3] The heaping up of citations here would be mere ostentation. The adjective " operational " I derive of course from Mr. Bridgman. See also in recent popular literature Mr. Eddington's *The Nature of the*

ture but a " reality." And besides Eddington—who, of course, has somewhat changed his views since this time—M. Meyerson invokes the testimony of Langevin, Borel, J. Becquerel, Weyl, and Marais to the same effect.

What a scientist thinks he is philosophically and what he really is are often quite different since the days of Kant. The deeper question of whether a belief in an external world of atoms and molecules is compatible with " operationalism " (scientific radical empiricism) and if so, in what sense, is not answered by the say-so of its proponents. M. Meyerson is of course aware of this and spends the greater part of his book trying to point out how a realistic ontology is implied by relativity. But we must here note that he does not discuss the possibility of a conflict between the methodological assumption which gave the special theory its peculiar complexion and the actual technique of the general theory, but on the whole considers the general theory to be what relativity essentially stands for. This raises a question which is not answered without separate study, for although the general theory was constructed to alleviate the awkward position in which the special theory left physical calculations,[5] and thus follows from it, nevertheless the methodological assumption

[5] That is, it gave no reason why one set of co-ordinates should be chosen rather than another. See Einstein's *Relativity*, N. Y. (Holt) 1920, p. 72 et seq. and ch. XXI. Cf. *The Meaning of Relativity*, Princeton, 1923, p. 65.

which was the point of departure of the special theory cannot apply to the general theory.

In brief the discord between the two parts of Einstein's theories—a discord which is not logical but epistemological—is due to the very aim and *raison d'être* of the general theory. Constructed to envisage the world from the point of view of any observer, to represent phenomena independent of a given system of reference, it directly contradicts the fundamental tenet of the special theory; which was that one could never properly escape some observer's point of view and that calculations which in the older physics had been made upon the assumption that points of view—systems of reference—could be neglected, were for that very reason in need of revision. But the general theory by using the Lorentz equations is able to give us measurements which are not functions of the point of view. But they can only be derived from measurements based upon experience and hence true of a special system of reference. That they follow logically is unquestionable—at least by us. That they are necessary, if we are to have a science of physics, is equally unquestionable. The only question which the philosopher can legitimately put is whether they do not transcend observation. An affirmative answer is obvious. But what then is their value? Is it to explain causally the behavior of moving bodies or to provide a unification of the measurements taken on individual systems of reference? The general theory seems to do both. But whereas such concepts as "gravitational fields" etc., are bound to be irrationals in themselves and no more inherently significant than "the force of attraction," what is perfectly clear is the fact that if the universe is as the general theory describes it to be, then the measurements of individual observers will be logically deducible from it—I assume of course the "truth" of the general theory. But this is mathematical deduction and not causal explanation. It is legalism and not causalism.

M. Meyerson is not of this opinion. There is, he maintains (*DR* 68 ff.), a passage from the realism of common sense to that of relativism. Taking an example from Eddington, he points out that the common-sense representation of, say, a chair is a well-defined object in nature, seen in some way from all points of view at once and not from a particular angle.[6] This absolute chair is invariant to experience and, says M. Meyerson (*DR* 70), corresponds to the "rigid and inactive" framework of immediate perception. Common sense abstracts the framework from the percepts and this leads us to the space of Galileo, Descartes, and Newton.[7] Einstein, having discovered that certain of the elements of that

[6] I. e., it is the chair as described by solid geometry, which is of course unobservable though perfectly intelligible. *If* the real chair is thus, then—because of the laws of classical optics—the seen chair will be thus and so.

[7] Yet there is literally nothing in common—i. e., no identity—between the real geometrical chair and the perceived chair, though there should be according to M. Meyerson's theory of reasoning.

space—distances and times—are not invariant to any system of reference pushed on to a framework, that of space-time, in which the variability of these elements was rendered harmless. It was an attempt, like that of common sense, to find " an invariant, something which substituting itself for fugitive sensation, would be more stable than it; the visual or tactile sense-chair may be totally transformed, may even disappear, while the object-chair will remain what it *is* " (*DR* 71).

But here again the object-chair is not empirically observable and though it may be the " cause " of the sense-chair, it is its cause only as a sphere is the cause of its circular shadow. The sphere and the circular shadow have not even shape in common, but we can infer logically the circular shadow from the sphere. It therefore belongs to a world which is not necessarily a world of realistic objects at all—although it may accidentally be one—and if it is reached through the observed objects, it on the face of it consists in nothing more than a positivistic harmonization or unification of appearances. To make it more than that necessitates the introduction of a new postulate, the postulate that that exists which implies the appearances which we find in experience. But such a postulate, if made, raises the whole problem of the realization of those implications, of the *modus operandi* of perception and the fusion of " implication " with " causation ".

The absolute entity of Einstein is plainly none of the data of perception, neither the sense-data nor the physical objects of common sense. For one thing, the world of perception, as M. Meyerson points out (*DR* 79), does not and could not afford evidence of a world in which the temporal dimension is isotropic.[8] Even if we could see chickens re-entering their eggs and men digesting their meals before eating them (*DR* 104), we should presumably see these series of events as a series, one occurring temporally *after* the other, so that it would take some time for a man to grow younger. Moreover the image of the world which common sense constructs is that of a world relative to a typical and usually human observer. And even when it grows sophisticated and divests the world of its secondary qualities, it imagines primary qualities of such a nature as to explain the secondary. It is, moreover, obvious that in dealing with the world of primary qualities for experimental purposes, the scientist is dependent upon symbols (percepts) which are by hyothesis not the entities he is interested in. These symbols are largely visual even in the case of entities like temperature and pressure, which are not normally perceived by the eyes. So that the logic of his procedure in dealing with this world again takes the form of a hypothetical syllogism in which the consequent is affirmed (through observation) in order to prove the ante-

[8] Einstein himself makes certain reservations about the isotropy of time. V. *Rev. Philos.* 53d yr., March 1928, p. 163.

cedent. We explain the world of secondary qualities by propositions which we then try to substantiate by the very phenomena they were invoked to explain. We assert, then, that if the explanations are true, the phenomena will be found. Finding the phenomena would not prove the explanations, though not finding them would disprove them.

It cannot be maintained that the ontological status of Einstein's space-time is entirely of this nature, nor is it modelled after the traits of the common-sense world. It is derived first from the proposition that there must be measurements " true for any observer " and second from certain mathematical considerations, as M. Meyerson points out, which have practically nothing to do with the world of perception but which arise from what he calls the needs of the reason. Thus perception shows him a world in which points of view are not negligible but determine in part the calculations which an observer will make from them. The passage from this to an invariant world structure can only be prompted by something not perceptual but intellectual. The reason demands an absolute, the senses do not provide one. But as long as human experience is perceptual, it will know nothing of measurements which transcend its own system of reference. If now a theory wished to be radically empiricistic, it would cling desperately to the unstable and variable pattern of perceptual life. But what science was ever content to stay there? It wants universal laws which are good for any system of reference and Einstein is no more reluctant than any of his confrères to abandon experience and construct such laws. To use Mr. Whitehead's phrase, which has now become idiomatic, nature is " bifurcated " at precisely that point where science ceases to be satisfied with a " special point of view " and seeks expressions which will have " general " applicability.[9]

Yet there are two kinds of bifurcation, or generalization. The first is that of what Reid called the Cartesian tradition, based upon the metaphor of substance and accident in which the " general " traits are possessed by the substance, leaving the special traits high and dry in an entirely different world of " appearance." The second is that of a system in which the special traits are necessary parts, as the position of any point on a sphere may be determined be reference to a set of co-ordinates passing through the centre, yet no two of which have the same co-ordinates. If the positions were perceptually known—like shapes or colors—it is obvious that they would change as one moved about the sphere, yet they would be determined (one might even say " caused ") by the general system of co-ordinates. Unless one knew that one was on a sphere and knew something of geometry, I do not see how one could ever arrive at a knowledge of one's position in terms

[9] Mr. V. F. Lenzen in his "Scientific Ideas and Experience," *Univ. of Calif. Pub. in Philos.* VIII, 175, seems to have demonstrated this point, applying it to Mr. Whitehead's philosophy itself.

of three co-ordinates from the perception of that supposititious datum, one's position. Yet should one by some brilliant imaginative feat—like that of Einstein in formulating the general theory—guess that one was on a sphere, it is clear that one's position (and hence everything implied by it) would be absorbed into the new theory and be *explained* by it. This type of explanation, however, would not be a relegation of the special traits to a realm of appearance, it would be the deduction of them from geometry. At the same time, if the theorist maintained that he was clinging to the radically empiricistic point of view, he would be in grave error. There would be bifurcation in his system as in any other, but it would not be " Cartesian " bifurcation.

Would such a theory be intelligible? That is perhaps for everyone to decide for himself. It would certainly be as intelligible as geometry, using the word as a synonym of " deduction " in general. It would at least permit us to say, " If the world is a sphere, then the changes in ' position ' logically follow." There may of course be other possible antecedents to that premise, but until one is found, we shall probably be satisfied with that. It would not be intelligible, however, if reasoning is a " cascade of equations " and causation the transfer of static qualities from cause to effect. But it is our private opinion that such a view of causation arose in mechanics from a metaphor based upon visual-tactile experience, expressed in the formula, *ex nihilo nihil fit*. We have already, however, tried to show cases of "determination," if not causation, in which the metaphor is inept and the dictum inapplicable. Hence we shall not expand our remarks here.

M. Meyerson points out that the Einsteinian absolute is determined by certain mathematical considerations. But mathematics, as we all know, cannot proceed without universals. And it is equally well known that a system of universals would be absolutely static: change would be foreign to it. But similarly universals are exactly those properties of entities which the entities have in common and which are therefore invariant to the properties which the entities have in particular. Thus arithmetic, as a science of order, presents us just those ordinal properties which all entities have regardless of their specificity. The same thing is true of geometry (which M. Meyerson maintains is essentially a science of space) [10] and hence any geometry would give one a picture of a space which is the invariant properties of all the objects in it. These invariants would constitute an absolute system.

As relativity has developed it has become more and more of a geometry. The burning problem of the general theory is of course that of gravitation. M. Meyerson indicates how vexatious this problem has been since the time of John of Salisbury. As we know, the problem arises for Einstein out of the

[10] This is not an unquestionable description of geometry, but we can accept it for the purposes of this essay.

existence of rotatory and accelerated motion. The motion of bodies in a gravitational field is accelerated in a manner which is independent of the material or physical state of the body. It has been calculated in the past from such properties as mass and distance alone. From this Einstein deduces the equivalence of the inertial and gravitational masses of bodies, a fact which had been known before but, as Einstein says, had not been "interpreted."[11] The interpretation must be made with a view to explaining the *necessary* equivalence between inertial and gravitational masses. The word "necessary" here means "logically deducible." Gravitational mass turns out to be a purely spatial property, for to the observer all that happens when the motion of a falling body becomes accelerated is that it approaches the earth more and more quickly, i. e., its distance from the earth becomes less and less, varying with a time factor. This is pure observation or legalism. But Einstein does not remain a legalist. He *explains* the acceleration by stating that something called a "gravitational field" surrounds the earth, and of course all other physical objects, with an "intensity" growing less and less as one goes outwards. What, however, can the "intensity" of a gravitational field mean if we are to retain the operational theory of meaning, which, it should not be forgotten, is the basis of the special theory? Simply that objects near the given object approach it more rapidly and those far away

[11] See *Relativity, the Special and General Theory,* pp. 76 et seq.

less rapidly and that objects far enough away do not approach it at all. But distances are purely geometrical concepts. This leaves time floating. If one weaves a time factor into one's geometry, one can absorb acceleration into it and mass as well. The distance between two objects in space-time will not then be represented by a simple straight line (along which one moves with uniform velocity) but a line which grows puckered, so to speak, as one approaches the physical objects (i. e., as acceleration, which is inevitable and calculable, sets in).

This may be called "geometry," if one will, but it is what Einstein has called "practical geometry" as distinguished from "purely axiomatic geometry."[12] Practical geometry is held by him to describe—and to allow one to deduce—the actual behaviour of physical objects in space. Does this mean that practical geometry is therefore realistic and not phenomenalistic? Einstein undoubtedly thinks it does, but it is clear that the ontological status of physical objects is unprejudiced by the laws which describe their behaviour. Their objective nature must be determined in the same manner whether they are located in space-time or in Euclidean space of the seventeenth century variety. All that has happened is that a particular geometrical system has been selected to describe them rather than another. The deeper question is whether an "operational"

[12] The philosophic reader will find this most congenially explained in Einstein's "Geometry and Experience," tr. in *Sidelights on Relativity,* London, 1922, esp. p. 32.

physicist has any right to a belief in the distinction between the real and apparent nature of things.

The great benefit to physics is the higher degree of simplification. For now from the characteristics of space-time the physicist can deduce the behaviour of moving objects, as it is observed, whereas from Euclidean geometry he could not. In M. Meyerson's language (*DR* 92 ff) such a space fuses the mathematical and the physical properties of things. But time, being the factor in terms of which acceleration is described, is also " spatialized," for all the points along a line will be point-instants and since time is a factor of motion and since motion can go in any direction, it looks to certain relativists as if space-time were isotropic in all its dimensions. And when this fusion is made, becoming turns into being, succession is illusory, and change becomes a purely human affair.[13] According to common sense and to the conscious experience of individuals who may perchance be relativists, time is irreversible. Some relativists, including Einstein himself and Weyl, recognize that for all the universe is four-dimensional, the time dimension is not quite on a par with the other three. Weyl says in fact that the universe should be spoken of not as having four dimensions

[13] *DR* 102. Note here the bifurcation into what space-time seems like to us and what it really is. If we are to be "operational," this bifurcation ought to go, for it is obvious that we could have no *empirical* knowledge of an isotropic time dimension. This does not mean that time is not isotropic, nor that science should be "operational."

but 3 + 1. Why is it, however, that relativists in general prefer to " spatialize " it? Because, says M. Meyerson (*DR* 106), our reason seeks identity. Space is indifferent to its contents, but time is apparently not. Our reason tries to overcome this. " Our reason," he says (*Ib.*), " does not remain stiff in such an attitude. Tout au contraire, elle cherche à expliquer les modifications que le temps conditionne dans les choses, ce qui signifie qu'en fin de compte elle suppose tout de même que, par suite de l'écoulement du temps seul, il ne devrait y avoir aucun changement. Ce qu'il y a au fond de cette recherche d'explications ou de causes, c'est donc une conception qui rend les objets indifférents à leur déplacement dans le temps, c'est-à-dire assimile, à ce point de vue, ce déplacement à celui dans l'espace. Il est tout aussi manifeste qu'à partir du moment où nous faisons entrer le temps dans nos calculs, ne fût-ce qu'en vue de la simple prévision, nous sommes obligés d'obéir, dans une certaine mesure, à la même tendance. Car nous représentons le temps par un symbole, comme une grandeur. Or, ce qui caractérise les grandeurs, c'est qu'elles peuvent croître ou diminuer—alors que le temps ne recule jamais, que nous ne pouvons donc lui prêter un mouvement régressif que dans notre imagination." When time shall have become assimilated into space, then the physicist will hope to deduce all physical events—if not all events whatsoever—from space-time geometry.

It is this drive towards an *explication globale* by means of spatial concepts—found, be is noted, only in the general theory—that M. Meyerson sees evidence for his thesis that the relativist, like the absolutist whom he has replaced, seeks a static eleatic real beneath the flow of phenomena, which will be their cause. For he feels that he has shown in his earlier work, *De l'Explication dans les Sciences* (Ch. VIII), how the search for the permanently self-identical has progressively developed into the more and more complete spatialization of all our concepts. It may begin with the simple observation that material objects displace themselves without internal alteration—though of course they do not according to the theory of relativity—it goes on to explain that fact by the continuation of an identity through space. The indifference of space to the " nature " of what it contains is the key to its popularity as an explainer. Curiously enough, since things are not changed by space, the only change that can be discovered will be in the spatial relations themselves and a change of whatsoever character—even psychical—will be based upon a change of position.[14] But again, M. Meyerson insists, purely spatial properties are deducible from geometrical premises

[14] It will be noted that the fundamental axiom of atomism is that no entity will change until " acted upon " by another entity. Change internal to an entity for no " reason " other than that it is the natural history of that entity to follow a certain course of change is not admitted by atomism. Hence indifferent space has to be assumed as a vessel in which such interaction is to take place.

alone. Whence relativity is in no wise a break with the general scientific tradition of Europe. Space-time is simply the new absolute which takes the place of space.

M. Meyerson nevertheless points out that a complete geometrization of nature can never be made. For one cannot deduce the existent from the universal. Relativism is limited in exactly the same manner as Hegelianism was limited or Cartesianism or as the Platonic construction of the world in the *Timaeus* was limited: by the necessity of an existence-postulate. The postulation, indeed the discovery, of existents is not a logical operation, an inference. But this objection would only hold good if Einstein were constructing an " axiomatic geometry." He insists, on the contrary, that he is using a " practical geometry," which, as he says, " rests essentially on induction from experience, but not on logical inferences alone."[15] Whether what he says is true or not may be open to question, but if it is true, then the argument that " geometry " will not afford an *explication globale* is only partly justified. Even an inductive geometry will contain assumptions and irrationals; but the margin between its conclusions and reality will be much smaller than that between axiomatic geometry and reality. The question becomes one of discovering the congruence between space-time geometry and facts.

[15] *Sidelights on Relativity*, p. 32.

In general discovery is made by direct observation, by inference from an observation to its "cause," and sometimes by noting the agreement of logical deductions with observations. Here a genuine difficulty arises. If space-time is an absolute "beneath" observation, then the first method is impossible. The third method is always formally fallacious though sometimes accidentally true. So that only the second method seems to be left.

What the space-time construction is required to explain is the world of the special theory. The special theory is built up to meet the demand of the radically experimental theory of meaning—"operationalism." If the special theory were an adequate explanation of observation, and if the general theory followed logically from it without the introduction of new postulates, then obviously the general theory would be based upon fundamentally the same data as the special theory. This, however, is not entirely true. We know that the special theory holds good primarily for certain limited cases, viz., cases of rectilinear non-accelerated motion. We know furthermore that the velocity of light is not constant when light enters a gravitational field. It will be admitted by us that the general theory is corroborated experimentally. The question before us is whether its concepts are definable as, say, "simultaneity" was definable for the purposes of the special theory. The notion of a gravitational or a magnetic field is to the point.

" ' If we pick up a stone and then let it go, why does it fall to the ground? ' The usual answer to this question is: ' Because it is attracted by the earth.' Modern physics formulates the answer rather differently for the following reason. As a result of the more careful study of electromagnetic phenomena, we have come to regard action at a distance as a process impossible without the intervention of some intermediary medium. If, for instance, a magnet attracts a piece of iron, we cannot be content to regard this as meaning that the magnet acts directly on the iron through the intermediate empty space, but we are constrained to imagine—after the manner of Faraday—that the magnet always called into being something physically real in the space around it, that something being what we call a ' magnetic field.' In its turn this magnetic field operates upon the piece of iron, so that the latter strives to move towards the magnet."[16]

It is obvious that all that is observable here is the acceleration of the falling stone or the piece of iron and an operationalist ought to be content with this. That the space between the earth and the stone about to fall, or the magnet and the piece of iron, is filled with "something physically real," we are only "constrained to imagine" if we refuse to be satisfied with what we observe. The movement beyond is apparently a movement out of positivism into ontologism. That Einstein has good reasons for invok-

[16] *Relativity*, p. 74.

ing what he later calls a " somewhat arbitrary " conception, I should not be presumptuous enough to deny. But these reasons are not operational. Aside from such a question of detail, however, is the larger question of the perhaps basic hypothesis of the general theory: the invariance of the laws of nature in all co-ordinate systems. This certainly could never be given an experimental meaning for the very reason that no observer could ever be on all systems at once. The best he could do would be to say that if the laws of nature were thus invariant, certain experimental results would be obtained which, as a matter of fact, are obtained. But that the laws of nature are thus and so remains an assumption. It is an assumption which unifies knowledge, but that knowledge should be unified has the same æsthetic character as Copernicus's assumption that Nature chooses easy means of performing her tasks, not difficult. Again, I am not presuming to object to this assumption; I am simply noting its character.

Though the general theory gives us a world which differs from that of the special theory, it does not follow that it is necessarily a world of ontological reals. That would all depend upon the ontological status of immediate perceptions. If they are " mental "—phenomena—then there is no *a priori* reason why space-time should not also be mental, whatever that might mean. I say this not to suggest that space-time is mental, physical, or neutral, but merely to invite one's attention to the fact that a group of cal-